the Forth Naturalist and Historian

Volume 21

Naturalist Papers

Book Reviews and Notes (Naturalist): Butterflies of the Millennium p62; Environmental Information in Scotland p62; Flanders Moss p16; Forth Estuary Forum p61; The Nature of Fife p16; Discovering the Firth of Forth p52; Man and the Landscape Symposia p62; The Effective Alternative p6; *The Glasgow Naturalist* p52.

Historical Papers

Book Reviews and Notes (Historical): Archive Photo Series p88; Bannockburn Years pp135-6; Barbour's Bruce p116; Menstrie Glen pp136-7; Stone Age Alpha p88; Carron Iron Works p134; Towards Democracy in Education p96; Blind Harry's Wallace p88

Forth Naturalist and Historian, volume 21

Published by the Forth Naturalist and Historian, University of Stirling – an approved charity and member of the Scottish Publishers Association. 1998.

ISSN 0309-7560

ISBN 1-898008-27-2

Supported by BP in Scotland.

Cover: front– The Wallace Oak, Torwood
       back– Raploch Village
By courtesy of The Smith Art Gallery and Museum, Stirling, and
       R. McCutcheon.

Printed by Meigle Printers Ltd., Tweedbank Industrial Estate, Galashiels.
Set in Zapf Calligraphic on Amber 100 gsm and cover cream Lustralux.

GLOBAL WARMING: WHERE ARE WE NOW?

S. J. Harrison

In 1997 the average temperature near to the surface of the Earth, based on more than a thousand climatological stations and available sea-surface temperature records, was 0.43°C above the 1961-1990 average (Parker *et.al.*, 1998). This was 0.6°C higher than the average at the end of the nineteenth century. During 1998, the months up to June were the warmest on record and July eventually became globally the hottest month ever recorded, and it is highly likely that the average for the current year will exceed that for 1997. In the Stirling area 1997 temperatures were well above average but 1998 has proved to be cooler. On the whole, the available climatological data provide a strong indication of an upward trend in the global average temperature, the effects of which have included:-

- the timing of the onset of spring in the Northern hemisphere, which is more than seven days earlier than twenty years ago. Satellite images indicate that spring foliage has been emerging earlier and that summer vegetation has been more verdant. Exotic species have begun to invade areas outside their normal distribution and many weeds are experiencing climatic conditions more conducive to their invasive habits. Higher air temperatures have caused a world-wide resurgence of diseases such as malaria and dengue fever, the latter being on the verge of entering Europe.

- Sea-ice around Antarctica has been melting quite rapidly over the last twenty years at the rate of 1.4 % cent per decade. The indications are that large areas of ice shelf have now disintegrated and an estimated 8000 km^2 have been lost over fifty years. The rate of melting of Arctic sea-ice has accelerated from 2.5 to 4.3 % per decade, and parts of the Arctic Ocean are now 1.0°C warmer than they were in the late 1980's.

- High summer temperatures have impacted directly on the tourist industry in the United Kingdom, resulting in an increase in earnings of the order of 15 %. Recent changes in the Scottish climate (Harrison, 1997) indicate a widening difference in climatic conditions between a wetter and windier west and a drier and sunnier east, which has obvious implications for the tourist industry (Harrison *et.al.*, in press). The reduction in winter snow lie on the Scottish mountains has had a deleterious effect on skiing on lower slopes but above 1000 m there has been sufficient snow to sustain the industry.

Although there remain a substantial number of climatologists who are sceptical of the evidence for global warming, the majority view is that an ongoing trend has been established and that action needs to be taken to alleviate its environmental and socio-economic impacts. Of the more dire predictions, changes in agricultural productivity could bring up to 70 million people to the brink of starvation, and there may be an increase in the number of people dying from disease and heat stress. Global warming has, therefore, been placed high on the international political agenda, but the emphasis has been on achieving political accord rather than on dealing with the reality of the problem being faced. While scientific opinion points towards a need to reduce emissions of greenhouse gases by as much as 60 %, the Kyoto conference, which was little more than political theatre, realised only an 8 % reduction over the European Union and a 7 % reduction from the USA, the latter conditional upon first-option terms regarding the trading in Russia's spare carbon emission permits. There are powerful lobbies in the USA resisting the implementation of the Kyoto agreements, with Republican members of the Congress trying to block any further funding for research into climate change, while funding has been made available to those scientists willing to undermine the case for global warming. Kyoto also failed to reach any agreement on emissions from aircraft and shipping, which are important sources of greenhouse gases.

The principal questions which have yet to be answered fully are (1) is the observed increase in temperature attributable directly to anthropogenic influences or is it simply a natural fluctuation and (2) are there other processes which will ameliorate or exacerbate the effects of enhancement of the Greenhouse Effect? In addressing these questions it must be remembered that prediction of the future course of climate change is based on mathematical models which are, by their very nature, no more than imperfect representations of an infinitely complex web of interrelated environmental processes.

Much of the warming has been associated with two important changes in elements of the atmosphere-ocean circulation. The Southern Oscillation (ENSO), referred to as El Niño, was responsible for the inflation of temperatures in the tropical Pacific Ocean, while the North Atlantic Oscillation (NAO) has brought warmer wetter weather to western Europe and to Scotland in particular. The current debate is whether such changes are a result of, or causal factors in, global warming. More recent studies have reopened the debate on the effects of externally forced climate changes resulting from fluctuations in the amount, and characteristics of, solar radiation arriving in the upper atmosphere. This which would appear to explain a significant proportion of the warming trend experienced after the mid-nineteenth century. However, Mann et.al. (1998) claim to have established beyond reasonable doubt that much of the increase in global temperature during the twentieth century can be attributed directly to anthropogenic factors. Current international agreements are unlikely to result in a significant reduction in emissions of greenhouse gases, and sources such as cement manufacture and catalytic converters are providing increasing emissions of carbon dioxide and nitrous oxide respectively.

The answers to the second question unfold as more research is undertaken into the contributing processes. While the scattering effects of marine and industrial sulphate aerosol in the lower troposphere appear to have offset some of the warming effects of greenhouse gases, the greatest concern is now being focussed on the role of ocean currents in determining long-term changes in climate. Heat is moved around the oceans in what is commonly called a 'conveyor belt', which is very sensitive to changes in temperature, density and salinity of the water. This is of particular concern in Scotland because of the very powerful influence exerted by the warm North Atlantic Drift. The effect of a warming of the Arctic Ocean is to release large volumes of fresh water into the North Atlantic which, being less dense than saline water, could well drive the North Atlantic Drift away from the west coast of Scotland. Should such a change occur, its onset is likely to be quite rapid, while at the same time the processes involved may be difficult to reverse. The impact on the Scottish climate would be severe, particularly during the winter months when conditions would be more similar to those experienced along the eastern seaboard of North America, where snow and frost are relatively frequent. Changes in ocean currents in the Pacific have already brought more cold water to the surface, which has resulted in as much as a 20 % reduction in the amount of heat being transferred into the atmosphere.

In conclusion, the last few years have witnessed a consolidation of the evidence for global warming and there is now little doubt that there has been an upward trend in temperature which began in the mid-nineteenth century and has accelerated over the last two decades. The implications for Scotland could be for largely advantageous changes in climate but the continuation of the warming trend could result in a change to a more severe climate regime. One fundamental problem, however, still remains and that is the identification of the cause of such changes. These can be attributed directly to changes in the atmosphere-ocean circulation, but it is by no means easy to establish the nature of the relationship between these and global warming. The indications are that there is a strong anthropogenic factor in global warming and it is imperative that a means is found to reduce emissions of carbon dioxide, methane and nitrous oxide. Such is the nature of international politics that it is highly likely that agreement on this issue will remain a distant prospect.

References

Harrison, S.J. (1997). Changes in the Scottish climate *Botanical Journal of Scotland* 49, 287-300.

Harrison, S.J., Winterbottom, S. and Sheppard, C. (in press). The potential effects of climate change on the Scottish tourist industry *Tourism Management*.

Mann, M.E., Bradley, R.S., and Hughes, M.K., (1998). Global scale temperature patterns and climate forcing over the past six centuries *Nature* 392, 779-787.

Parker, D.E., Horton E.B., and Gordon, M. (1998). Global and regional climate in 1997 *Weather* 53, 166-175.

BOOK REVIEW (Naturalist)

The Efficient Alternative. Agnew, P.W. 1994. Tarragon Press, Ravenstone, Whithorn. 93pp. ISBN 1-870781-07-4. £5.95.

This is a hard-hitting frontal assault on what the author sees as the mismanagement of the energy industry and the vested interests which have hindered the development of efficient energy policies and supply alternatives. Pat Agnew has an industrial background and was, for more than 20 years, a lecturer in mechanical engineering at Glasgow University. While the book is very much a personal statement arising clearly from not inconsiderable frustration, it is thoroughly researched, informative and well argued. The author's approach is summarised as "how we can do away with nuclear power, reduce pollution, conserve natural resources and save money" with which few would argue. The introduction outlines the false assumptions and poor decision making which have shaped energy supply in the UK today. He lists, amongst others, the "false" assumptions that coal is a dirty fuel, that society need more electricity to improve the quality of life and that we need more nuclear and gas powered stations in order to reduce emissions of greenhouse gases. The answer is encapsulated in the two words "improved efficiency". The following chapters examine the history of the National Grid and the critical events which have shaped energy supply. Agnew questions the wisdom of increasing dependence upon the use of gas-fuelled power stations and the biasing of the market towards the energy produced by nuclear power stations. The third chapter has the emotive title "Economic growth – the god that failed" and questions the underlying need for growth. Surely a mature economy, like a mature adult, has a need for stability, not further growth. Chapters four through to six examine nuclear power, fossil fuels and renewable resources, and look very closely at the efficiency and real sustainability of these as sources of energy.

A strong case is made for the use of renewable resources such as water, wave and wind power, alongside reductions in energy consumption. The final three chapters examine alternatives for the future and deal with increasing the efficiency of energy conversion, the role of politics in directing the future of energy supply and demand, and ways of reducing energy costs without the need for nuclear energy.

There are several books on the market which address such issues many of which, like this one, express very strongly held views. Unfortunately, in many cases the arguments have been based too much on emotion and not enough on scientific principle. Agnew's background has provided him with excellent credentials to address this topic which, in combination with an obvious passion for the subject, makes for a compelling read. The final parting shot has an Orwellian feel to it when the Department of Energy are exhorted to "be prepared to publicise the truth and not allow the public to be misled by the vested interests that they themselves have created".

S. J. Harrison

THE WEATHER OF 1997

S. J. Harrison

After a cold and exceptionally dry start to the year, January 1997 being the driest for 200 years in the UK, the following months were exceptionally mild. The mean maximum air temperature was above average for every month except May and June, while the mean minimum air temperature was below average only in January (Fig. 1). Rainfall was above average in only four months, February, May, June and December, and the annual total was only 95 % of average (Fig. 2). Over the UK as a whole, 1997 was the third warmest year this century behind 1990 and 1949, and again there was much talk about the effects of global warming on the climate. The identification of an oscillating weather condition in the Atlantic (North Atlantic Oscillation) has confirmed that changes in the strength and persistence of the mid-latitude westerly circulation are the primary cause of recent warm and moist winter weather in the British Isles.

Temperature and rainfall values in the following refer to Parkhead II although reference is also made to the records from Bridge of Allan.

January   Exceptionally dry, and cold

Snow fell overnight on the 1st/2nd and again on the 3rd and 4th. The 6th to the 10th were dull, cold and dry, the daytime temperature struggling to rise above freezing and reaching only 1.0°C in Bridge of Allan on the 8th. Strong south-westerly winds reached Scotland late on the 10th and snow was falling by the late evening. The 11th was a grey and miserable day but the temperature rose rapidly in mild tropical air. The daytime temperature topped 11.0°C between the 12th and 14th but the weather stayed dull and damp. Night frost under clearing skies occurred briefly on the 20th but the cloud cover returned on the 22nd and the weather was cold and raw until the 24th. There were patches of freezing fog by the morning of the 25th (–4.5°C). From the 28th, night-time temperatures fell sharply, reaching –5.2°C in Bridge of Allan by the morning of the 31st.

February   Windy and very wet, but generally mild

Rain began late on the 1st in a freshening south-westerly breeze, which set the pattern for much of the rest of the month. The sequence of wet and windy weather was broken only by brief calmer and clearer periods during which night temperatures fell, and there were sharp frosts on the 5th and 6th (–5.4°C Bridge of Allan on the 5th). The wind turned briefly into the north-west on the 7th, bringing blustery showers of sleet and snow. The wind freshened south-westerly again late on the 9th heralding the start of a wet 72 hours. The total rainfall for the period amounted to 48.9 mm (48.3 mm Bridge of Allan). Many fields on the Carse of Stirling were under water and the Allan overtopped its banks on the 12th. Heavy rain fell all day on the 17th, followed by heavy showers on the 18th, then two days of heavy rain on the 19th and 20th, amounting to an exceptionally wet spell. Over the four days 17th-20th, 88.1 mm of rain fell (86.1 mm Bridge of Allan), bringing severe floods to parts of Scotland, which were accompanied by gale force winds on the 19th (maximum gust at the University 39 kts (gale force)). By the morning of the 21st, a cool showery westerly wind had become established, which held sway until the evening of the 23rd when there was yet more rain in very strong winds. The breeze died away on the 26th, bringing frost and a little overnight snow. The month ended with two more very wet days on the 27th and 28th (22.0 mm; 25.5 mm Bridge of Allan). The total rainfall over the twenty-eight days was more than 250 % of the long-term average over much of southern Scotland.

March   Changeable and very mild

Rain fell all day on the 1st (20.2 mm) in a strong westerly wind and was followed by blustery showers of sleet and hail on the 2nd. The 3rd was calm with night frost, but less settled weather returned until the 6th. There were night frosts on the 8th and 9th (–3.2°C). Cloud returned on the 10th and the weather became rather dull at times, but mild in a light south-westerly breeze. The maximum temperature stayed above 10.0°C for almost all of the rest of the month, reaching 14.0°C on the 15th (15.1°C Bridge of Allan). By the 14th, the weather had turned rather damp with low cloud and drizzle, with relatively infrequent sunny spells. Night frosts returned by the morning of the 21st. Unsettled weather moved in from the west late on the 21st and persisted until the 27th. The wind became very strong on the 26th, gusting to 37kts (gale). After the 28th there was a fresh and quite sunny end to the month.

April   Quite warm and very dry.

This was the warmest April on record at Parkhead and the rainfall total of 25 mm was less than half of the average for the month. There was a showery westerly airstream over the first two days but the wind changed to a cooler north-westerly on the 3rd and the temperature had fallen to –3.8°C in Bridge of Allan by the morning of the 4th. Snow and hail fell later in the day. Rain fell on the 5th and 6th and it remained cloudy and dull until the 8th. The 9th to the 16th were bright and sunny days and maximum temperatures topped 20°C in Bridge of Allan on the 12th and 14th. The weather then became changeable from the 17th, and the 23rd was the wettest day of the month (11.1 mm). Scotland was affected by a cold easterly breeze on the 25th and 26th and the daytime maximum temperature failed to reach 8°C in Bridge of Allan on the latter. Warmer air had arrived from the west by the 27th restoring temperatures to the seasonal average.

May Both cold and hot; wet at times

The first two days were sunny and exceptionally warm. The maximum temperature reached 23.3°C in Bridge of Allan on the 2nd (24°C in Edinburgh). However, on the 3rd there was a sharp fall in daytime temperature to 12.1°C. The 3rd and 4th were very wet (48h total 25.0 mm), and thunder was heard during the afternoon of the 4th. This was followed by a spell of very cold weather in a northerly polar airstream. Snow fell on the 5th and 6th, which caused problems on the roads in north-east Scotland. Some of the showers on the 7th and 8th fell as hail. By the morning of the 9th the air temperature had fallen to –2.4°C in Bridge of Allan, marking the last air frost. Rain returned late on the 9th and the weather remained unsettled with further rain at times over the following four days. The weekend of the 17th and 18th was cold and wet with low cloud and rain, which was very heavy at times, and accompanied by thunder on the afternoon of the 17th. Bridge of Allan registered 23.1 mm of rain over the weekend. Heavy rain fell on the 20th in a freshening easterly breeze and the daytime temperature reached only 10.0°C in Bridge of Allan. The cloud cover gradually cleared away from the 22nd and the month ended with a spell of very warm and sunny weather. The maximum temperature reached 28.4°C in Bridge of Allan on the 30th.

June Wet. Warm at first but becoming cooler

A fresh easterly breeze blew over the first three days which were sunny but cool. After a very warm and sunny day on the 4th, cloud increased from the south and the 5th and 6th were rather humid with isolated thundery outbreaks. The following four days were unsettled with occasional showers. The last ground frost was recorded on the morning of the 9th. The 11th was wet and cold (maximum temperature 13.8°C and 21.1 mm of rainfall), but was followed by another brief warm spell from the 14th. Cool and wet weather returned on the 18th. Very unsettled weather arrived late on the 24th but the worst of the rain had cleared Scotland by the 27th after which the weather became sunny and warm until the 31st. For much of the British Isles this was the wettest June this century.

July Warm and relatively dry

The first three days were dull with spells of locally heavy rain. Severe flooding affected northern Scotland on the 1st and the Aberdeen to Inverness railway line was closed when embankments were washed away. There was a relatively warm and dry spell from the 4th to the 9th and the maximum temperature reached 25°C. From the 9th there was a mixture of showers and sunny spells, although conditions became very muggy on the 12th and 13th. The weather remained unsettled until the 16th after which there were seven days of hot and mainly dry weather, although there was a short thundery spell during the evening of the 20th. The daytime temperature reached 28.7°C in Bridge of Allan on the 21st. The fine weather came to an end late on the 22nd as cloud and rain arrived from the west. Rainfall amounts were, however, relatively small and there were long sunny spells. By the 28th, the temperature in Scotland was falling in a strengthening, and showery, south-westerly wind which brought blustery showers on the 30th and 31st.

August Very Warm and dry

The weather was remarkably warm, maximum temperatures rising above 20°C on all but six days. Although warm, the weather was occasionally rather dull and by the 7th had turned very muggy with the daytime temperature rising above 25°C. The temperature on the 10th rose rapidly in a very humid southerly airstream and had reached 30.2°C in Bridge of Allan on the 12th. The weather broke on the 13th and torrential rain fell in a thunderstorm during the late afternoon (27.5 mm). However, the temperature remained high over the following days, although they were a little less oppressive. Minimum temperatures were remarkably high and the overnight temperature dropped only to an exceptional 17.7°C between the 20th and 21st. On the 21st a freshening south-westerly breeze brought an end to the muggy weather. As the clouds cleared, the night temperature fell to 5.4°C in Bridge of Allan by the morning of the 24th. The weather became unsettled and much cooler for the remainder of the month, with occasional rain and long sunny spells, and on the 31st the maximum rose to only 15.7°C, in marked contrast to the rest of the month.

September Sunny and warm, and generally rather dry

The weather over the first eight days was unsettled and there was heavy rain on the 2nd and 3rd (24.7 mm). There was bright and clear weather from the 9th but with an autumnal chill in the cold polar air. On the 11th, showers, some of hail, fell in a strong north-westerly breeze and the daytime temperature reached only 12.5°C on the 12th. There was heavy rain on the 13th, and between the 14th and 15th there were further falls in a strong south-westerly wind which gusted to 35kts (gale) at the University. The rain continued into the 15th and 16th, resulting in a 48h total fall of 31.0 mm. This was followed by a lengthy spell of calm, clear and dry weather in Scotland, which lasted from the 17th to the end of the month. Under clear night skies, minimum temperatures fell towards freezing, reaching 0.3°C in Bridge of Allan by the morning of the 20th, which also saw the first autumnal ground frost (–0.4°C). The weather was generally warm and sunny, but between the 21st and 25th the days began with dense fog. A freshening southerly breeze began to blow on the 28th, and by the morning of the 29th the minimum temperature had fallen to only 14.4°C. Over much of the southern half of the UK this was one of the driest Septembers this century.

October Sunny: Warm at first but turning cold

The first four days were sunny and dry and the maximum temperature reached 18.4°C on the 4th. The weather changed on the 5th at the start of an unsettled spell which lasted until the 12th. Rain was intermittent for the most part and the minimum temperature remained above 12.5°C on the 5th and 6th. Torrential rain began to fall during the evening of the 9th, and by the 10th 24.2 mm had fallen. On the 12th a weak northerly airstream affected Scotland, bringing a sharp drop in temperature and the first nocturnal air-frost in Bridge of Allan. but cloudy and wet weather returned on the 14th. The 15th to the 18th were dull and wet days, but mild in a variable southerly airstream. The cloud base remained low, barely rising above 65 m on the 16th. The four-day rainfall total 14th to 17th amounted to 35.4 mm. Colder weather began to set in on the 19th and by the 20th, a cold north-easterly breeze had developed which brought the first snow to the local hills. As the breeze died away and the clouds cleared, there were night frosts. The minimum temperature had fallen to –5.8°C in Bridge of Allan by the morning of the 29th. Days were bright and sunny after early morning ground fog.

November Mild and rather damp

Unsettled weather was in control for much of the month, with mainly dull weather and relatively rare sunny interludes. When the cloud cover did clear briefly, night temperatures fell below freezing, but there were only two air-frosts at Parkhead over the course of the month. Frost was accompanied by fog on the morning of the 9th. A fresh southerly breeze began to blow on the 15th which imported moist tropical air from the Azores into Scotland. Minimum temperatures exceeded 10.0°C locally between the 16th and 20th and the daytime maximum reached 16.1°C on the 15th. The wind freshened and gales and widespread flooding had caused damage throughout Scotland by the 18th, although conditions in the Stirling area were less severe. There was a spell of heavy rain on the 20th (12.4 mm). After the 23rd there were five very dull days before an easterly breeze cleared the air on the 29th. The last day of the month saw a welcome change to bright sunny weather.

December Mild but changeable

The first three days were bright and clear in a light north-westerly breeze, and there were moderate night frosts, the temperature falling to –5.7°C in Bridge of Allan by the morning of the 1st. Air temperatures increased sharply from the 5th in a freshening south-westerly, the maximum reaching 12.2°C on the 6th, and rain was a feature of the weather on most days. There was a sustained spell of wet weather from the 9th to the 11th (23.5 mm). Frost returned by the morning of the 12th, which was accompanied by fog on the 13th. Milder air from the south-west saw a return to cloud and drizzle but a strengthening easterly wind then blew between the 15th and 18th. The weather over this period was cloudy and dull, and felt very raw. The wind gusted to gale-force at the University on the 17th as sleet and snow swept eastwards across Scotland. However, the cold snap was short-lived as milder weather was restored on the 18th, which was a particularly wet day (22.2 mm). The weather remained dull over the following days. Central Scotland escaped the worst of the Christmas gales, but a wet spell, which started late on the 23rd and finished late on Christmas Day, brought a total rainfall of 37.0 mm. The weather improved a little after Christmas and the 27th and 28th were much brighter as the cloud cover cleared away, only to return on the 29th.

WEATHER NOTES

Noteworthy Scottish Weather Events over 1997

Heavy rain and floods during February
There were two spells of particularly heavy rain, between the 10th and 12th and the 19th and 20th. Rain was combined with strong winds which made driving very difficult in places. Eskdalemuir (Dumfriesshire) registered 79 mm on the 19th/20th while the Butt of Lewis recorded a gust of 88 kts (hurricane force).

Snow in Scotland May 5th and 6th
There was severe disruption on the roads in Grampian Region.

July 1st Floods in North-East Scotland
There was prolonged heavy rainfall over Scotland which led to flooding around Elgin, Forres and Nairn. A great amount of damage was done to agricultural crops, several roads and railways lines were cut, and properties were damaged by flood water. More than 70 mm of rain fell in 48hr.

Floods in Scotland September 16th
Gales and heavy rain affected much of Scotland on the 16th and conditions in western Scotland were particularly severe as more than 75 mm of rain fell in some areas.

Climate Change and its Effects on Scottish Tourism

An analysis of climate change in Scotland has been undertaken in an attempt to generate a meaningful picture of what the future may hold for tourism in Scotland. The study has been based on historical analogues and a GIS-based Digital Elevation Model. Specific attention has been focussed on winter snowfall and summer wetness as these have a major bearing on visitor activity in Scotland. The analysis suggests that, should the winter climate shift to a more westerly maritime character, then lowland areas would experience more frequent snow-free months. As elevation increases then the reduction in snowlie becomes more pronounced, but above 1000 m the trend is reversed

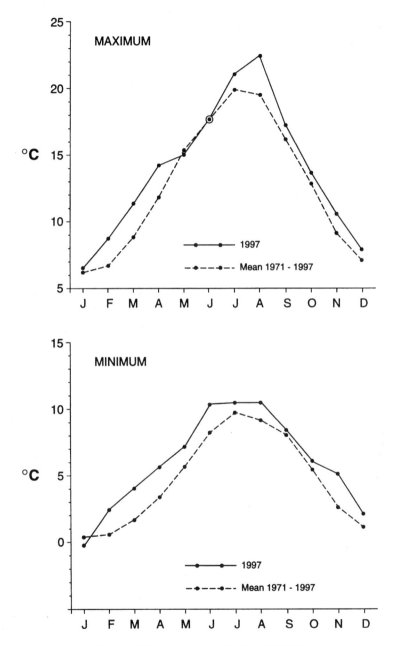

Figure 1 Air temperatures at Parkhead I 1997.

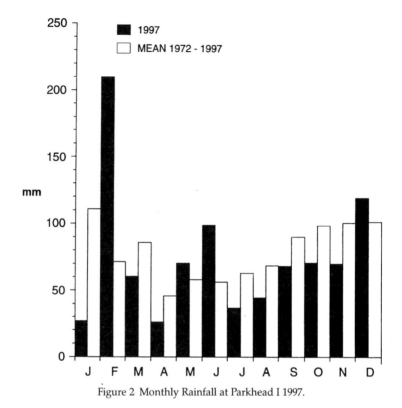

Figure 2 Monthly Rainfall at Parkhead I 1997.

and the highest ground experiences some of the smallest reductions in Scotland. Analysis of summer wetness indicates a potential reduction in the number of wet days by as much as 10 % in lowland areas, but over higher ground this increases to 20 %. Thus it would appear that the upland areas may well offer the tourist a greater probability of being able to appreciate the scenery on offer.

Rainfall Measurements in Western Scotland

The initial encouragement and guidance provided to the Lochaber Raingauge Network on behalf of the Royal Meteorological Society, and the efforts of George Clark as coordinator, have together ensured that more than 40 people in the west of Scotland now have a focus for their interest in their local weather. The data may also provide, in the long-term, an invaluable contribution to the understanding of rainfall-topography relationships and may challenge scientists to review the assumptions they have made in this field. An analysis of some of the data generated by the Network has indicated that local topography, and not elevation, is the most important factor in determining the spatial distribution of rainfall.

Regional Climate of Central and Southern Scotland

An analysis of the principal features of the climate of that part of Scotland lying south of the Highland Boundary Fault has been published as part of a new study of regional climates in the British Isles (Wheeler, D. and Mayes, J. 1997 *British Climates: A Regional Approach*. Routledge: London). All the studies use the latest 1961-1990 climatological averages. Dr Harrison describes not only the principal spatial patterns of temperature, rainfall and snowfall, airflow, visibility and sunshine in the southern part of Scotland, but also notable weather events such as the Strathclyde Floods of December 1994 and the Glasgow Storm of 1968, and particular local features such as the Forth Valley Frost Hollow and the East Coast Haar. References to old manuscripts add an interesting historical dimension to the study. The climate of the northern part of Scotland, and the islands, is described by Marjory Roy, formerly of the Meteorological Office in Edinburgh.

Access to Parkhead Monthly Data

The monthly mean maximum and minimum temperatures, and monthly rainfall totals for Parkhead climatological station on the campus of the University of Stirling can now be obtained via E-Mail at no charge. Schools wishing to access these data should E-Mail Dr Harrison at *sjh1@stir.ac.uk*.

Acknowledgement

This paper is based on the Annual Climatological Bulletin which is produced by the Department of Environmental Science at the University of Stirling.

BOOK REVIEWS/NOTES (Naturalist)

Flanders Moss

A meeting of the British Ecology Society's MIRES Research Group at the University of Stirling from 30th June to 5th July 1998 included working study/survey visits to – the species-rich fen at the south of Loch Lomond; the high level (550 m) blanket bog at Hart Hill in the Campsies; and a two day one to Flanders Moss.

Saturday 4th July was a symposium of eight presentations–
Geomorphology – David Smith, University of Coventry.
Peat Stratigraphy – Jim Dickson, University of Glasgow.
Vegetation – Alan Booth, Central Scotland Surveys.
Hydrology – High Ingram, University of Dundee.
Archaeology – R. Hingley, Historic Scotland.
History – Ken Mackay.
Peatland Conservation – Philip Imertzi, SNH.
Management and Monitoring – Tim Jacobs, SNH.

Organised by John Proctor. The Forth Naturalist and Historian intends to publish a proceedings.

L.C.

The Nature of Fife. Edited by Gordon R. Corbet for the Fife and Kinross Board of Scottish Wildlife Trust. Scottish Cultural Press, Edinburgh. 1998. 356pp., illustrated, including colour. ISBN 1-84017008-5. £14.95.

In an easy to read style this is a comprehensive work on the diversity of wildlife and habitats of Fife by specialists in their fields – including George Ballantyne who has contributed to the *Forth Naturalist and Historian* with flora surveys on West Fife in volume 12, and Balmerino in 14.

It includes a comprehensive inventory of species of plants, fungi and animals so far recorded in Fife and adjacent seas. The inventory is available at £7.00 separately on disk from Fife Nature, Fife House, Glenrothes.

Contents of the book – include – Geology and landform, R. MacGregor; Climate, N. Elkins; Landscape and history, Whittington and Smout; Landward coast, R. Crawford; Shore, estuaries and sea, Bentley and Fairlamb; Farms and fields, Warrener; Woodland, Ingram and Larson; Freshwater, S. Pritchard; Heathers and grassland, A. Irvine; Living with man, Corbet and Ballantyne; Conservation, F. Spragge; an inventory of the flora and fauna of Fife.

L.C.

FORTH AREA BIRD REPORT 1997

C. J. Henty

Sixty-four contributors appear this year, some sent notes direct to the author, others via the RSPB local group. The extensive use of record cards has greatly helped the compilation of notes by species. In addition, others have assisted in the wildfowl counts and the breeding birds survey and I have extracted some records from the logbook of the SWT hide at Kinneil though not all contributors are identifiable. Notable records for this year include the first Rosefinch (a singing male), Bittern, a summer Little Ringed Plover and the first Clackmannanshire Honey Buzzard. At least eleven Quail were calling on the carse and a brood was seen. Most contributors – and many non-birdwatchers – will be aware that Ospreys have been nesting in the area for some years and it is now felt sensible to acknowledge this publicly in a summary of breeding success. Lesser Blackbacked and Herring Gulls now have well established colonies on the roofs of whisky bonds, these are prominent but difficult to census. On the estuary in autumn there were few Skuas but a modest passage of waders and a massive Swallow roost developed above Cambus.

This report is compiled from a larger archive of records submitted to the local recorder under the national scheme organised by the Scottish Ornithologists Club. The area covered by the report comprises the council areas of Falkirk and Clackmannan together with Stirling, excluding Loch Lomondside and other parts of the Clyde drainage basin. Please note that we do not include the Endrick water, i.e Fintry and Balfron. Records from Carron Valley Reservoir are published here but it is proposed that Clyde should cover all the forest south of the reservoir. Observations are not spread evenly, the inland part of Falkirk is once more neglected and the extensive and often inaccessible hill area in the north of our area has had only sporadic coverage although a second likely breeding area for Dunlin has been found.

Though 1997 was overall a very mild year it started with snow in early January and severe frosts at the end of the month. Heavy rain in early and mid February caused extensive flooding, including the Forth overtopping its banks on both sides of the Devon, and the continuing unsettled weather dominated March though there were a few frosts early on. From mid April it was warmer than usual and there was only half the normal monthly rainfall, however, May was very varied with snow and hail in the first week leading to wet and cold conditions and then warm and sunny in the last week. Through June and July dry sunny spells alternated with rain though the third week of July was hot and dry. Most of August was very warm and dry, becoming unsettled late on. Spells of rain and wind in early September gave way to calm high pressure weather and some morning fog but it soon became unsettled in early October until an anticyclone in the last week gave northeast winds, sunny but with night frosts. Mild but wet and windy conditions dominated most of November and December though there was a brief sunny and cold spell midway and also easterly gales with sleet and snow in mid December.

The 1997 information on the breeding numbers of common species come from two studies of mapped territories. One is a Common Birds Census plot east of Doune, this is 87 Ha of undulating, dry-field farmland at about 70 m a.s.l, mixed pasture and winter cereal, which is referred to as "Doune CBC" in text. The other is a Waterways Birds Survey along 5 km of the R.Devon at Alva which has much damp scrub surrounded by mixed pasture and arable, referred to as "Devon WBS", or, for species that are not fully mapped, as "5 km of lower Devon".In addition the Breeding Bird Survey, based on transect counts, is now sufficiently extensive to calculate numbers of birds recorded per ten kilometres for several habitat types and these are regularly mentioned in the species paragraphs. Note that the "Urban" term includes suburban areas with large gardens. For less common species I can sometimes mention data in terms of the numbers of pairs or apparently occupied territories for particular locations. Several observers send in a list largely or entirely for their home locality, much of this information is not appropriate for these annual reports but it is valuable to have on record and I am keeping them in a special file. At the moment there are fourteen such lists referring to the whole district from Falkirk to Killin.

For many species the records sent in are very unrepresentative of their general distribution, this applies particularly to very common species or to those that are secretive or breed in inaccessable places. Readers can consult the the Check List published in the *Forth Naturalist and Historian* vol 15, but in addition I have in this report put, after the species name, a coded summary of general distribution – which often apparently contradicts the detailed records that are published for the year.

> *B* - Breeding status, widespread (in more than five 10 km squares)
> *b*   "   "   , local , scarce (in fewer than five 10 km squares)
> *W* - Winter status, widespread or often in groups of more than ten.
> *w* -   "   "   , local, scarce (local and usually fewer than ten in a group)
> *P* - Passage (used when species is usually absent in winter, *P* or *p* used for widespread or local as in winter status)
> *S* or *s* - a few species are present in summer but do not normally breed.

Thus *BW* would be appropriate for Robin, *B* for Swallow, *p* for Ruff and *SW* for Cormorant. No status letter is used if a species occurs less than every other year.

An asterix (*) in front of the species name means that all records received have been quoted.

The SOC has pressed for a more systematic vetting of records of species that are unusual locally, this area now has an informal panel of five – C. Henty (Recorder), W. Brackenridge (Dep. Recorder), J. Crook (local SOC rep), A. Blair and D. Thorogood. The judging of national UK or Scottish rarities continues as before, but we have produced for the upper Forth a list of species that are scarce locally and where the records need to be supported by either a full description or sufficient evidence to remove any reasonable doubt. This list and a background explanation have been circulated to a hard core of observers and can be got from the recorder at SOC meetings or by post. Any species which is a vagrant to the area, and most of those which are asterisked in this report, will come into this category.

The organiser for the inland waters part of the national wildfowl counts (WEBS), has made available an account of the results for the winter 1996-1997. These often contribute to the species accounts and there is also a separate summary which concentrates on localities.

There is an ever-increasing amount of information coming in: records on the standard species cards need only to be sorted and I would urge observers to use these wherever possible (putting several records for one species on a single card); records on sheets, whether written, hand-typed or computer-typed, need to be either retyped onto a computer database or cut and pasted onto species sheets. This is time consuming and the recorder can no longer do this systematically without extensive help from contributors; otherwise these records will be scanned on arrival and only those items seeming to be salient will be transferred to the database, all the original sheets will be kept on file but that information is very difficult to unearth and inevitably some uncopied records will in fact be important but remain hidden. Appeals for assistance will continue!

The following abbreviations have been used : AoT - apparently occupied territory, BoA - Bridge of Allan, c/n - clutch of n eggs, BBS - Breeding Bird Survey, CBC- Common Bird Census, CP - Country Park, F - Female, GP - gravel pit, J - juvenile, L. - Loch, NR - Nature Reserve, M - Male, ON - on nest, Res - Reservoir, SP - summer plumage, V - Valley, WBS- Waterways Bird Survey, WG - Wildlife Garden, Y - young.

This report has been compiled from records submitted by:

P. & M. Ashworth, A. Ayre, M. Adam, B. D. Allan, M. Anderson, B. W. Barker, B. Bear, M. V. Bell, N. Bielby, Birdline Scotland, A. Blair, W. R. Brackenridge, R. .A Broad, G. J. Brock, D. M. Bryant, G. Bryson, R. Bullman, M. Callan, D. J. Cameron, R. Chapman, D. A. Christie, Z. Clayson, M. Cooper, S. D. Dick, H. M. Dott, A. Downie, K. & R. Egerton, D. S. Fotheringham, C. J. Henty, T. Jacobs, R. Jones, H. Kerridge, M. Kobs, G. & E. Leisk, A. K. McNeil (AKM), W. McEwan, L. J. Mallett, J. Marshall (JMr), A. McKillop, G. Mason, J. Mitchell, J. Nimmo, R. Nudds, D. Orr-Ewing, R. L. Osborn, G. Owens, R. K. Pollock, D. Rees, H. Robb, P. W. Sandeman, J. Sankie, S. Sankey, R. E. Scott, R. Shand, A. Smith, P. Stirling-Aird, D. Thorogood, A. Thiel, B. R. Thomson, M. Trubridge, H. Weir, J. Watson, J. Wheeler, M. Wilson, T. Young, R. Youngman.

Thanks are due to the Deputy Recorder, W. R. Brackenridge, for assistance and advice on records, to A. Thiel for putting a batch of records on computer, to Dr S. J. Harrison for a copy of the Annual Climatological Bulletin (1997), and to P. Stirling -Aird for data from the Raptor Study Group.

RESULTS OF THE BBS SURVEYS FOR CENTRAL REGION
(Based on a comprehensive summary by NB.)

Readers will have noted that in this year's report extensive use is made in the species accounts of results from the Breeding Birds Survey, these are in terms of the frequency of occurence of a species along linear transects in several habitat types. This use is now possible since in 1997 the number of 1x1 kilometre squares surveyed has more than doubled to a total of twenty-three and there is a much fairer coverage of the habitat types (the British Trust for Ornithology district is not quite the same as the SOC recording area since it includes some squares in neighbouring parts of Perth and Kinross, however these are very similar in type to the rest). Each square is visited twice in spring/summer, a total of two kilometres on a set route is walked per visit and all birds noted in 200 metre sections; a standardised habitat survey is done on another visit. In the main report I have presented selected results, calculated as birds per ten kilometres of habitat, for the major habitats where it is likely that the birds are breeding locally.

Each 200 m section and the birds noted in it have been attributed to one of five major habitats – Mountain and moorland (=moor), Moor/conifer woodland edge, Conifer woodland, Farmland, Urban/suburban. Broadleaved woodland occurs mainly as copses in farmland whilst conifer woodland includes both young plantations and mature woods

Eighty-eight species were seen overall, with an average of 27 per square but a great variation from four on blanket bog to 46 on mixed farmland, numbers of individuals varied similarly from five to 135.

Most Abundant Birds on Four Major Habitats

Moor	Conifer	Farmland	Urban
Meadow Pipit	Willow Warbler	Rook	Starling
Carrion Crow	Chaffinch	*Black-h Gull*	Blackbird
Black-h Gull	Coal Tit	Chaffinch	Jackdaw
Skylark	Wren	Starling	House sparrow
Starling	Goldcrest	Wood pigeon	Carrion Crow
Common Gull	Siskin	Swallow	*L.Black-b Gull*
Curlew	Robin	Feral Pigeon	Rook
Rook	Great Tit	Carrion Crow	Greenfinch
L.Black-b Gull	Blue Tit	*Common Gull*	Swift
Red Grouse	Redpoll	Blue Tit	Blue Tit
Mallard	Wood pigeon	Jackdaw	Feral Pigeon
Wheatear	Carrion Crow	Willow Warbler	Willow Warbler

I have put in italics those species where the great majority of records presumably relate to birds commuting to feed, not breeding. Another hazard in interpretation is that no account has been taken of differences in conspicuousness (it is possible in principle to use BBS data to correct for this but the procedures have not yet been developed). Thus large species will be overrepresented in open country, and a voluble small bird compared to a silent one. Nevertheless, these data are the best comprehensive indications available of the quantitative distribution of birds over our area.

The lists of the 12 commonest species contain no real surprises for most habitats, however in Urban areas Willow Warbler appears above Magpie, Chaffinch, Collared Dove, Robin, Wren, and Dunnock – this seems odd in general experience but may be due to one area containing patches of scrub. Further expansion of this project would be most worthwhile and I would urge more people to take on unsurveyed squares; the most taxing part is the habitat form!

1997 contributors were: M.A., B.D.A., R.B., W.R.B., Z.C., P .Crayton, R.C., S. Harley, A. Hibbert, C.J.H., L. Johnstone, P. McManamen, R. Osborn, L. O'T, S.S., A.T., J.W., R. Young, T.Y.

WILDFOWL REPORT (1996-97)

This report concerns the inland waters part of this area's Wetlands and Estuary Bird Survey (WEBS) organised by NB and is a condensed version of a fuller report by him.

WEBS is a monthly waterfowl census under the auspices of the British Trust for Ornithology (BTO) and the Wildfowl & Wetlands Trust (WWT), it runs from September to March inclusive. For this report 'wildfowl' includes Divers, Grebes, Cormorants, Herons, Swans, Geese (excluding Pink-footed and Greylag for which the WWT organises separate counts), Ducks and Rails

This report covers the area occupied by the new local government councils of Stirling, Falkirk and Clackmannanshire (the 'region'). In total, 114 still water sites, 136.5 km of river and 24.4 km of canal were counted by 44 counters.

Still Water Sites

Standing water in Central Region amounts to 7693 hectares or 2.9 % of the area.

The following table consists of matched monthly data taken from 14 sites in the top 25. Those sites holding fed Mallard have been excluded.

Month	1995/6	1996/7	1997/8
September	1814	1583	1756
October	3359	2039	2454
November	3699	3235	3037
December	4513	3955	3396
January	2885	4477	3332
February	2750	2771	2940
March	1549	1646	1930
Totals	20804	19706	18845

This season's numbers are down 4.6 % on the previous but this only applies from November to January and is only really marked in the three top sites of Gartmorn Dam, Gart Complex, and Airthrey Loch.

Turning to individual sites, the top nine along with monthly averages are listed below:- (previous seasons figures in brackets)

	Site	Average
1. (1)	Gartmorn Dam	996 (1300)
2. (3)	Gart Complex	366 (243)
3. (5)	Airthrey Loch	279 (181)
4. (2)	Lake of Menteith	267 (264)
5. (4)	Loch Earn	206 (217)
6. (9)	L.Venachar-Achray	170 (141)
7. (6)	Blairdrummond Park	162 (178)
8. (12)	L.Dochart-Iubhair	155 (123)
9. (13)	Doune Ponds	121 (149)

The above table excludes sites where Mallard are reared and released for shooting.

As shown above, Gartmorn is still far and away the most populous site, holding 37 % of all still water birds in the region.

Linear Water Features: Rivers & Canals

This season all of the canals in the region were counted.and the river length increased to 125.5 km due to the R. Teith between Doune and Callander being included. Some data are still to be sent in but these waters contribute at least 22.5 % of inland wildfowl.

WEBS contributors to these data additional to report list were: M. Cooper, P. Dearing, A. Hibbert, D. Mason, D. Minard, L. O'Toole, J. Peterson, D. Series, N. Sharpe, D. Shenton.

SYSTEMATIC LIST

Codes – S, F and C indicate records from Stirling, Falkirk and Clackmannan-shire "Districts".

RED-THROATED DIVER *Gavia stellata (b,w)*
F   2 Bo'ness 11 Jan. Kinneil: 3 on 2 Jan, 1 on 18 & 19 Jan; 1 on 10 Aug & 20 Dec. 1 Kincardine Bridge 28 Dec (DMB DT GO AB DSF).
S   2 L. Katrine 21 Mar. 1 L.Achray 21 & 28 Mar. (NB DAC). 1 Glen Finglas 12 Apr (SS). 1 L.Lubhair 29 Apr. 1 Killin 4 May to 3 Jul, 2 on 9 May (PWS).

BLACK-THROATED DIVER *Gavia arctica (b,w)*
F   1 Bo'ness 11 Jan (DMB). 1 Kinneil 19 Jan, 30 Sep & 8 Oct (AB DSF CKM).
S   2 pairs & a single seen on 2 lochs in breeding season, 2 nests failed through flooding (DAC BDA RES DOE).

LITTLE GREBE *Tachybaptus ruficollis (B,w)*
F   Kinneil: 1 on 23 Jan; 17 Sep to 14 Dec, max 6 on 11 Nov. Skinflats 17 Sep to 27 Dec, max 4 on 28 & 30 Oct (CJH GO DSF DT DAC AB). 2 on

R.Carron at Larbert 7 Jan & 3 on 7 Feb (MA).
C   1 calling at Cambus Pools 20 Oct (WRB). 17 Gartmorn Dam 20 Oct & 19 on 12 Nov (MC).
S   4 Airthrey 9 Mar. 4 Cocksburn Res 22 Mar, pair + 2Y 2 Jul & 6 Aug (AT JS JMi). Pairs L.Voil & Hutchison Dam in May, Arivurichardich Res on 14 Jun (DT WRB SS). As usual regular on wildfowl counts on highland lochs, max 8 L.Lubnaig 28 Jan & 7 on 24 Oct. 2 Killin Marshes 28 Nov was 1st WEBS record (NB). Scarce on main rivers, 3 Lecropt 25 Jan & 1 Cambuskenneth 28 Nov (DAC AT).

GREAT CRESTED GREBE *Podiceps cristatus (b,W)*
F   20 Blackness 18 Oct (CJH). 1 Skinflats 2 Nov (MVB).
      Kinneil monthly max: Jan 74, Feb 10, Mar 7, Apr 4, May 0, Jun 2, Jul 34, Aug 32, Sep 69, Oct 103, Nov 100, Dec 48 (DT DMB AB).
C   4 Gartmorn 15 Jan, 9 on 17 Mar; 19 on 12 Nov (still 17 on 6 Dec) presumably included juvs (MC).
S   At Carron Valley Res 2 on 12 Jan & 5 on 9 Feb, 3 pairs raised 1Y (WME GJB). 1 Lake of Menteith 29 Jan, 11 in BP on 26 Feb & 22 on 23 Mar, only 4 pairs in Apr; 17 (4 J) on 26 Sep, still 6 on 29 Dec (NB DT DAC). 2 L.Watston 18 Mar (CJH). 2 Pairs W. Loch of Daldorn 9 Mar (BWB). Pair L.Coulter 4 Mar. Pair with 1J Vale of Coustry (Blairdrummond) 26 Sep (NB).

*SLAVONIAN GREBE *Podiceps auritus*
S   1 Carron Valley Res 10 Oct (RKP).

*FULMAR *Fulmarus glacialis (p)*
F   Kinneil: 1 on 10 Aug & 2 on 30th; 3 on 5 Sep & 4->W on 6th(DT BDA).

*MANX SHEARWATER *Puffinus puffinus*
S   1 Kinneil 15 Sep (DSF).

GANNET *Sula bassana (p)*
C   At Cambus on 25 Sep a Juv came from down river & left inland over Airthrey (CJH).
F   14 Juv Kinneil 26 Sep (GO).

CORMORANT *Phalacrocorax carbo (S,W)*
F   71 Skinflats 2 Nov (MVB). 65 Higgins Neuk 15 Feb & 133 on 6 Oct (DSF).
C   164 S.Alloa roost 2 Oct & 162 on 30 Nov (CJH AT). 9 Gartmorn 6 Dec (MC).
S   17 L.Earn 28 Dec. Max Lake of Menteith 15 on 29 Jan & 20 on 28 Oct (NB). Regular in winter on upper Forth: 6 at Teith confluence 9 Feb, 9 there to 6 km upstream 10 Mar (AMK RC). At Airthrey Jan-Mar, max 9 on 14 Mar (MVB).

*SHAG *Phalacrocorax aristotelis*
F   1 Higgins Neuk 25 Oct (DSF).

*BITTERN *Botauris stellaris*

F   1 Skinflats reedbed 31 Jan & 1 Feb, once stayed in full view for 20 min, also did cryptic posture with vertical bill. Full description included dark crown and streaks on centre and sides of neck. (GO AB JMr WRB).

GREY HERON *Ardea cinerea (B,W)*

F   13 Skinflats 30 Jun & 22 on 21 Sep (GO MVB).

S   31 used nests Blairdrummond (Nyadd) 22 May (CJH). Pair nested on Airthrey Loch, 2Y (MK). 31 L.Earn 28 Dec (NB). 11 BoA 4 Oct (AD). During snow by the A811 at Kippen on 3 Jan, one hunted on the verge within 3 m of traffic (DT).

MUTE SWAN *Cygnus olor (B,W)*

WEBS total up 32 % on 96-97 season (NB)

F   Pair + 6Y on Union Canal at Falkirk 10 Jun; Pair +3Y on Carron at Larbert 8 Jun (MA). Pair + 4Y Larbert Loch 4 Sep. Pair Little Denny Res 16 Sep (NB). 33 on Forth/Clyde Canal at Bonnybridge 14 Feb (AA). 20 Skinflats 28 Feb (GO).

C   47 included 14 juvs at Gartmorn 11 Sep, 112 there on 21st & record 122 on 12 Nov (CJH MC). 1 nest fledged 5 at Cambus, 2 pairs on 17 Mar. 17 on Devon WBS 12 Apr, pair reared 4 there, also pair + 8Y from upstream (CJH). Pair raised 5Y Tullibody Pond (NB).

S   28 Craigforth 15 Mar – might be same as 23 above the Teith confluence on the 10th (DT RC). 27 Lake of Menteith 29 Dec (NB). Pair at Airthrey with 8 juvs on 21 Sep (MK). At Cromlix 18 Sep, pairs with 3J at Lodge Pond & at House Pond. 10 (6J) Vale of Coustry (Blairdrummond) 26 Sep. Pair Hutchison dam 22 Feb (WRB).

WHOOPER SWAN *Cygnus cygnus (W)*

F   10 Kinneil 8 Oct (CKM) was the earliest & very transient herd, on 6 Nov 5 flew in from E and continued W (GO). 24 Larbert 7 Dec (AB). A yellow ringed adult at Dunmore on 29 Jul (DSF) may be one of 2 at Cambus 14 May (RJ), the bird at Alloa Inch on 22 Jun (DMB) or at Kennetpans on 20 Sep (CJH), or, indeed, the yellow ringed adult that summered at Kinneil last year.

C   12 Tullibody 9 Feb & 9 Mar (PMA). 11 Gartmorn 1 & 12 Nov (DAC MC).

S   Widespread on highland lochs. 50 Killin in Jan (PWS). 21 (5J) L.Dochart 28 Jan, 26 on 3 Apr, 13 on 15th, 4 on 25th, 4 very late nearby on 29th & a straggler on 20 May (NB PWS DOE). 20 Carron Valley 31 Dec (RKP).

On Carse of Stirling 24 Kippen 20 Jan (HK) seem to have moved through Feb to Gargunnock (Birkenwood) with max of 28 on 11 Mar, last 15 on 14 Apr (DR DAC DOE NB). A separate herd further east at Drip carse peaked at 16 on 29 Mar & probably were the 15 at Craigforth on 17 Apr (AMK).

On upper Forth, 1 on 21 Sep & 2 on 23rd might have summered (RC MT), otherwise 1st of autumn were 3 ->W Killin 7 Oct. 19 L.Dochart

14 Oct & 27 on 28 Dec (PWS NB), a neck collared bird here had been marked as an adult F in Iceland in 1994 and was later seen: Ireland, Oct 94; Orkney, Oct 96 & Glen Lyon, Nov 96; Orkney, Oct & Nov 97. 27 Kippen 29 Dec (TY). 12 Drip Carse 1 Dec, 12 on Teith on 30th, 16 Carron Valley Res on 14th &13 Lake of Menteith on 29th (RJ ZC WME NB).

Counts of juvs in distinct herds gave: Spring, 27 % Juv. Autumn 19 % Juv. However, any comparison may be biased since no carse herds were aged in spring and these often have very few juveniles. At L.Lubnaig on 24 Oct 2 Ad were accompanied by 6 Juv – all similar sized so probably a large family (NB CJH).

PINK-FOOTED GOOSE *Anser brachyrhynchus (W)*

The Goose Study Group ceased operating after the l997-8 season and MVB is no longer able to summarise records, thus the account here is largely based on non-systematic coverage and is much less reliable.

In Jan, 2540 at Lecropt on 2nd and 3000 at Thornhill on the 25th probably included the same birds, since a full carse count on the 23rd totalled 4000. In March large flocks were reported from the Lake of Menteith to Blairdrummond with a whole carse count of 4300 on the 23rd; there continued to be no reports east of Stirling. However, in April there were up to 3000 in the Buchlyvie-Gartmore area 9th to 17th and in addition 500 at Skinflats on the 18th and 1610 at Alloa Inches on the 20th – this a typical spring feature. The last flock had dwindled to 50 by 3 May and there was the usual visible movement with 100 flying W over Stirling on 25 April.

In autumn 4 at Cambus on 8 Aug were very early, the main arrival was 18th to 21st September with moderate flocks widespread, maximum 780 at Skinflats on the 21st. The last group seem to have stayed in the Kincardine Bridge-Clackmannan area at least to 22 Nov. On the carse of Stirling the largest flocks were 700 at Buchlyvie on 18 Oct, 700 Aberfoyle on 21 Dec and 540 Blairdrummond on the 21st. The early winter total seems unlikely to be much greater than 1300, much lower than last year.

BEAN GOOSE *Anser fabalis (W)*
F   100 L.Ellrig 19 Feb (JN). Around Slamannan: 51 on 1 Feb (GO); 100 on 31 Oct, 127 on 7 Dec (MA GO); max 157 on 11 Nov feeding in flooded pasture, a record flock (NB).
S   35 Carron Valley Res 26 Oct (WME).

*WHITE-FRONTED GOOSE *Anser albifrons (w)*
S   1 Lecropt 1 Jan (DT), 1 Thornhill Carse 11 & 14 Feb (DR). All were Greenland race.

GREYLAG GOOSE *Anser anser (b,W)*

Substantial flocks were noted in the north of the area with 200 at L.Venachar on 19 Jan and at Killin on 7 Feb. Full counts on the carse of Stirling gave 1100 on 23 Feb and 520 on 23 March; there were individual flocks of 300 at Aberfoyle on 29 Jan, 400 Drip carse on 15 March and 120 Thornhill carse on 6 Apr (the last, except for 2 on R.Devon 10 May).

Numbers were low early in the autumn but there sems to have been a late influx: after 35 flew W at Ashfield on 25 Oct there were 120 at Gartmorn on 1 Nov, 200 L.Coulter on the 11th, and 278 at Kennetpans on 14 Dec.

CANADA GOOSE *Branta canadensis (b W)*
　　　WEBS 97-98 season total up 30 % (NB).
C　　21 Cambus Pools 9 Sep (CJH).
S　　44 Vale of Coustry (Blairdrummond, biggest flock to date) 28 Jan, 9 on 28 Oct (NB). 8 L.Venachar 25 Jan (with Greylags) & 19 from 10 to 20 Nov (DJC). 9 L.Mahaick 19 Mar was return to breeding site (NB). 14 ->SW Ashfield 30 Sep (WRB). 14 ->W Buchlyvie 1 Oct (DAC). 42 Buckieburn Res 10 Oct, 20 Lake of Menteith on 28th & 22 Glen Finglas on 31st (NB DOE). 27 Lecropt 16 Nov & 12 on 13 Dec (DT DAC). 7 Thornhill Pond 20 Jan & 3 on 27 Apr (DOE).

BARNACLE GOOSE *Branta leucopsis (w)*
F　　Skinflats: 15 ->W 22 Sep, 26 on 28 Sep & 12 on 30th, 10 on 11 Oct (GO DSF AB DT). 62 ->SW Kinneil 26 Sep (BDA GO).
C　　2 Alloa Inch 20 Apr & 2 on 2 Oct (DMB CJH). 2 (with Greylags) Gartmorn 1 Nov (DAC).
S　　20 ->S Stirling & 11 ->E Carron Valley Res 27 Sep (DMB). 2 Lecropt 31 Dec (MVB). 2 on Forth around Cambuskenneth Feb to Apr & Nov-Dec, apparently feral residents. 2 at mouth of R.Allan 12 Jan had dark grey necks (AT - presumably some hybridisation, Ed).

*BRENT GOOSE *Branta bernicla*
F　　1 Skinflats 30 Nov (GO).

SHELDUCK *Tadorna tadorna (b,W)*
F　　105 Higgins Neuk 26 Jan & 420 on 6 Sep (DSF). Moult flock at Kinneil totalled 5067 on 16 Aug; 1810 at Skinflats on 14 Sep & 540 Kinneil on 18th, total only 322 in Dec (DMB CJH MVB). 129 Skinflats 22 May, 1st brood (11) on 21st, other broods were 5,8,11,12 on 28 May & 9,6,14,8,4 on 12 Jul (AB GO).
C　　147 Alloa Inch 4 May, 125 Tullibody Inch 6 Jul (DMB). 2 pairs on Devon WBS 15 May, last 2 on 25th (CJH). 3 Gartmorn 17 Mar (MC).
S　　2 pairs Cambuskenneth in Apr were highest up Forth (AT). 1 ->E Airthrey 13 May (DMB).

WIGEON *Anas penelope (b,W)*
　　　1166 Forth Estuary in Feb (DMB). WEBS totals of 464 on rivers in Feb (NB).
F　　Kinneil: max 500 on 2 Feb, 45 on 28 Mar; 1st of autumn 8 on 17 Aug, 300 on 20 Oct (DMB DT). 94 Higgins Neuk 26 Jan (DSF). Skinflats: 106 on 9 Feb, last 3 on 25 May; 2 on 6 Sep, 86 on 16 Oct (MVB AB GO).

C 844 Gartmorn 15 Jan, 360 on 6 Dec (MC). 2 Cambus Pools 24 Aug (WRB). 150 on lower Devon 21 Dec (GEL).

S Max Gart Lochs (Cambusmore) 225 on 20 Feb, 10 on 1 Aug & 200 on 17 Oct (NB PWS). Other large loch counts included 135 L.Venachar 20 Jan. There are more on the upper Forth between the Teith and Kippen, max 302 on 14 Jan (CJH NB RC). 1 Nest Torrie Lochan (BWB).

GADWALL *Anas strepera*
 More records over whole district (Ed).

F 4 Skinflats 10 Mar & pair 4 to 15 Apr; 14 on 14 Dec (AA GO AB).

C Pair Gartmorn 13 Feb & from 21 Sep to 6 Dec, 6 on 20 & 25 Oct (MC PMA DOE). 3 (2M) Cambus Pools 22 Mar, pair to 20 Apr & M on 26th (WRB DMB DAC).

S 2 Carron Valley Res 21 Sep (WME). 1 L.Mahaick 24 Nov (NB).

TEAL *Anas crecca (B,W)*
 1045 Forth Estuary in Dec (DMB). 840 inland in Nov (NB).

F Kinneil: 120 on 28 Mar; 1 on 8 Aug & 30 on 29th, 200 on 18 Oct. 200 Skinflats 9 Feb, 6M to 26 May; 9 on 8 Aug & 120 on 31st, 140 on 2 Nov (DT BDA CJH MVB GO).

C Few on Inches, 210 Gartmorn Dam 15 Jan but only 68 13 Feb (MC). 117 on Devon, Alva-Dollar, 18 Jan; last, pair on 3 Apr (RN GEL CJH)

S High numbers on inland lochs, WEBS counts of 388 in Oct & 500 in Nov, max of 166 L.Laggan 19 Nov, 120 L.Macanrie 19 Oct & 102 L.Dochart on 24th. 68 Cambuskenneth 28 Nov (AT).

MALLARD *Anas platyrhynchos (B,W)*
 619 Forth Estuary in Dec (DMB). WEBS total 3805 inland in Oct (NB).

F 165 Skinflats 11 Jan & 213 on 14 Dec (MVB). 180 Kinneil 29 Aug & 150 on 14 Dec (DT AB). 262 Larbert 21 Oct (MA).

C 22 AoT on Devon WBS, 17 in 1996 (CJH). 430 Gartmorn 15 Jan & 264 on 20 Oct (MC).

S 234 Airthrey 3 Jan & 282 on 16 Nov, 1st brood 9 Mar, median 8Y in 10 broods (AT MK). 6 pairs per sq km Doune CBC. 322 Blairdrummond 23 Dec. About 1500 released at 7 shooting sites around Dunblane (NB).

PINTAIL *Anas acuta (W)*

F Skinflats: 62 on 1 Mar, last 1 on 22 May; 1 on 4 Aug, 15 on 16 Oct & 46 on 27 Dec (GO MVB). Kinneil: 16 on 28 Mar, last 7 on 15 Apr; 1st autumn on 24 Aug, max 20 on 5 Oct (DT GO).

C 2M Tullibody Inch 22 Mar (CJH).

S 2M Gargunnock 25 Feb (DR).

Area Summary

Jan	Feb	Mar	Apr	-	Aug	Sep	Oct	Nov	Dec
52	39	80	16		9	16	35	48	46

SHOVELER *Anas clypeata (p)*

F 2 Skinflats 21-28 Feb, 2 pairs 11-22 Apr; pair bred with 5Y seen 26 May, brood probably stayed to 5 Sep; 1 on 16 Oct (GO). 3 Grangemouth 14

Sep & 4 on 21st (DMB). 3 Kinneil 22 Feb & 11 Apr, M or F to 29 Jun; 3 on 8 Aug, 5 on 12th, last on 1 Sep (GO DMB BDA DT).

C   F Gartmorn 17 Mar (MC). 5 Cambus Pools 19 Jul, last on 6 Sep (CJH WRB).

S   M Lake of Menteith 22 Mar (DAC)

POCHARD *Aythya ferina (W)*

F   6 singles around Grangemouth Jan, May, Oct (AS DT GO).

C   7 appeared on floodwater, Cambus,16 Mar (WRB). 42 Gartmorn 6 Dec (MC).

S   22 Vale of Coustry 29 Jan (NB); 28 L.Watston 13 Feb (CJH). 2 pairs L.Achray 12 May (DOE).
Highest monthly autumn counts: 10 Carron Valley Res 21 Sep & 45 on 26 Oct, 70 L.Walton 4 Nov, 32 L.Venachar 22 Dec (WME MF NB).

TUFTED DUCK *Aythya fuligula (B,W)*

F   47 Black Loch on 7 Feb & 59 on 10 Oct (NB).

C   3 pair + M on Devon WBS (CJH). 6 Cambus Pools 5 Apr, 2 on 6 Sep (WRB). 40 Kersiepow pond 5 Mar (NB). 164 Gartmorn 16 Feb & 98 on 6 Dec (MC).

S   188 on Forth at Cornton 10 Jan (CJH). 75 L.Earn 28 Jan (NB). 1 nest Ashfield & 2 at Torrie Lochan (WRB BWB). 60 Gart 1 Aug (PWS). Late autumn counts low, max 53 Lake of Menteith 29 Dec (NB).

SCAUP *Aythya marila (w)*

F   Kinneil: 5 on 19 & 22 Jan, 4 on 1 Feb (AB WRB); 5M on 16 Jul then max 6 from 31 Aug to 13 Oct & a remarkable 36 on 16 Oct. M Skinflats 21 May & 12 Oct (GO DAC DT).

S   F Carron Valley Res 21 Sep (WME).

EIDER *Somateria mollissima (w)*

F   7 (5M) Carriden 23 Mar (AS). Pair Kinneil 22 Mar & 5 Apr, M on 4 May; F on 30 Nov (GO DT AB). Pair Kincardine Bridge 8 Apr & M on 9th (DSF). 2 M Skinflats 16 Oct (GO). 3M Blackness 21 Mar; 7 on 3 Aug & 2 on 27 Oct (GO AB CJH).

GOLDENEYE *Bucephula clangula (W)*

54 Forth Estuary in Feb (DMB). WEBS total inland 383 in Jan (NB).

F   29 Carronshore 22 Jan. 15 Skinflats 23 Mar, 5 on 8 Jul (early) & 22 on 22 & 27 Oct; 14 Kinneil 22 Feb & 27 on 16 Oct (AB GO). 48 Black Loch 4 Mar & 33 on 12 Dec (NB).

C   62 Gartmorn 15 Jan & 43 on 6 Dec (MC). 19 on Devon at Dollar 23 Feb (RN). 12 on Devonmouth flood 16 & 22 Mar (WRB CJH).

S   125 on Forth at Cornton 5 Jan (CJH). 44 Cambuskenneth 9 Feb & 52 on 8 Nov(AT). 58 (14M) Lake of Menteith on 26 Feb. 36 L.Venachar 21 Mar & 22 L.Ard, 33 L.Dochart/Iubhair 30 Mar (NB). No May reports.
1 R.Teith 30 Sep (ZC). 52 Cambuskenneth 28 Nov (AT). 59 Lake of Menteith 29 Dec (NB). 28 % M (n=171) in March.

*SMEW *Mergus albellus (w)*
S   M L.Dochart 28 Jan & on L.Iubhair 2 & 25 Feb. M L.Dochart 27 & 28 Dec (NB DAC).

*LONGTAILED DUCK *Clangula hyemalis*
S   1996 M & 2F at Lake of Menteith 27 Mar (NB).

RED-BREASTED MERGANSER *Mergus serrator (B,W)*
    39 Forth Estuary in Dec (DMB).
F   Last Blackness 8 (4M) on 23 Mar (AS). 1st Kinneil 11 Sep, 16 on 29th & 25 on 1 Nov (GO DT). 17 Skinflats 9 Feb, 20 on 2 Nov & 18 on 14 Dec (MVB). 29 Higgins Neuk 30 Nov (DSF). 4 on F/C Canal at Falkirk 11 Jan; 1 on R.Carron at Larbert 12 Jan & 9 Feb (DM MA).
S   10 Cambuskenneth + 7 above Stirling Bridge 12 Jan (AT AMK). Unusually frequent on upper Forth in winter: 9 from Jan-mid Mar up to Arnprior & 1 Kippen 25 Oct. In spring at Lake of Menteith, L.Katrine (RC TY DAC HR).

GOOSANDER *Mergus merganser (B,W)*
F   36 Black Loch 11 Nov (NB). 5 Skinflats 5 May; 1 on 2 Sep, 11 on 14 Oct & max 15 on 26 Nov (BDA GO AB).
C   10 Tullibody Inch 20 Apr (DMB). At Cambus 2F+6Juv on 22 Jun, 13 on 19 Oct & 20 on 22 Nov (PMA CJH DAC). 19 on Devon at Dollar 6 Nov (RN).
S   22 Lake of Menteith 29 Jan, largest loch count except 26 (roost) Gart Loch 25 Feb (NB). Max Cambuskenneth 38 on 12 Jan & 24 on 16 Dec (AT). 29 Allanmouth 9 Feb & 21 on 9 Nov (AMK DT). On Teith up to Doune: 18 on 23 Feb, 38 on 28 Oct & 45 on 26 Nov (ZC). Totals on the upper Forth between the Teith and Kippen: 28 in Jan, 21 on 10 Mar (RC MT DAC). 1st ad M of autumn at L.Lubhair 24 Oct (NB).
    2 pairs bred Doune CBC (NB). In spring/summer noted at L.Doine, L.Lubnaig, L.Katrine, L.Chon, L.Ard, L.Achray, Lake of Menteith, Ashfield, Lanrick, Gleann A'Chroin (DAC HR DOE WRB CJH).

*RUDDY DUCK *Oxyura jamaicensis (b)*
F   2 Black Loch 12 Dec (NB).
C   Gartmorn: 2 on 15 Jan, F on 25 Feb & 28 Mar; 2 from 1 Nov to 6 Dec (MC PMA AT DAC).

*HONEY BUZZARD *Pernis apivorus*
C   1 Tillicoultry Glen 31 May (DMB). Circled overhead as close as 30 m showing 'translucent' wrist patches against light, underwing heavily barred and the longish, pale tipped, tail had a terminal bar and two others near base; rest of plumage dull brown with underparts slightly paler. Head was small and protruding more than Buzzard. When gliding the wings were held below the horizontal, the bird left toward Menstrie. *(The first documented record for Clackmannan, Rintoul and Baxter make only a general statement in their Vertebrate Fauna of Forth, Ed.)*

RED KITE *Milvus milvus*

> Of the 19 birds released in 1996, 8 attended a communal roost near the release cages during the 1996/7 winter and 11 are assumed to have dispersed. 9 were located at wintering grounds in: southwest Scotland (2), Lanark, Northern Ireland (3), Cumbria, Yorkshire and Devon. 2 of the dispersed birds are known to have returned to the release area in March and April 1997 and 2 territorial first year pairs were located.
>
> In late July 1997 a further 18 birds were released. By October a single communal roost had formed which through the winter was attended by 19 birds, 10 had been released locally in 1997, 7 were local 2nd year birds and 2 were wild bred from Easter Ross. (L. O'Toole, report slightly edited).
>
> Singles seen Flanders Moss 15 May, Dunblane 24 Sep & Gleann an Dubh Corrie 23 Oct & 11 Nov (TJ AD DJC).

HEN HARRIER *Circus cyaneus* (b, w)

> One coastal record. 15 males and 10 Ringtails noted, omitting repeated records.

F   1 Skinflats 20 Aug (GO).

S   1 Cock Hill 6 Mar, Gargunnock Hills 5 Apr, Ben Venue 26 Jul. 1 Flanders Moss 6 Jul & 3 at roost on 14 Feb. Many singles on Carse of Stirling 1 Jan to 6 Mar and 14 Sept to 29 Dec. On Braes of Doune & nearby 17 Sep to 21 Dec. 1 Dumyat 7 Jan, 1 Kippen Muir 4 Mar & 7 Dec. (NB RB DMB MVB WRB DJC DAC DOE CJH HK RLO DR DT).

GOSHAWK *Accipiter gentilis*

S   1 Carron Valley Forest 9 Sep (GJB).

SPARROWHAWK *Accipiter nisus* (B,W)

> Many records throughout area, including built up areas in Stirling and Falkirk. Few noted in midsummer when it is presumably secretive. Breeding records from Skinflats, L.Ard, Braes of Doune, Doune CBC (DT JW AB DOE NB et al).
>
> Perched under bird table in Stirling in Feb & Dec (RJ). Seen chasing Chaffinches, Magpies (DJC DAC). Perched bird shook wings at an approaching Grey Squirrel (AT).

BUZZARD *Buteo buteo* (B,W)

> As breeding bird: widespread & increasing S, scarce C, no proof F.

F   9 Torwood 4 Mar (AB). Around Falkirk: 4 Wallacebank Wood 19 Apr & present to Aug (AS); otherwise in Apr, Sep & Dec (JW DT). 1 Bonnybridge 21 Jan & 1 on 23 Feb (MA).

C   1 Menstrie 9 Apr, 1 Gartmorn 28 Mar & 11 Sep (AT CJH).

S   In main breeding range to W & N, largest group was 4 Invertrossachs 3 Aug . Frequent Braes of Doune, estimated one pair per sq km (DOE CJM DAC). Wintered on Carse of Stirling, 8 Lecropt 12 Jan, 9 on 4 Oct & 8 on 17th (DT); along Forth at Kippen 4 in Jan-Feb & 6 on 21 Sep (DAC TY). 6 Ashfield in Mar & 5 Dunblane 15 Jul (WRB NB). 9 BoA 15 Feb & present through summer (AT CJH). 5 Airthrey 20 Sep (DMB).

GOLDEN EAGLE *Aquila chrysaetos (b,w)*
S   8 territories checked, all occupied by pairs; 5 successful reared 6Y (PSA). No records outwith highlands.

OSPREY *Pandion haliaetus*
F   1 Skinflats 4 Jul, arrived from N (mobbed by Herring Gulls), left SE (GO). 1 ->E Carronshore 20 Jul (AB).
S   1st seen 2 Apr, last 10 Aug (DOE LJM et al). Five pairs held territories of which 3 laid eggs and reared 9 young – good success (RSPB). 1 Killin 16 May & 11 Aug (PWS). 1 Carron V Res 2 Jul to 24 Aug (AKM JW). 1 ->SW Ashfield 25 Jul & 1 Doune on 31st (WRB).

KESTREL *Falco tinnunculus (B,W)*
Difficult to make significant observations, hence greatly underrecorded.
C   Pair at nest Tillicoultry Glen 1 Jun (AT).
F   Through year at Skinflats (AB GO). Feeding young Kinneil 10 Jun, 5Y fledged 16 Jul (AS).

MERLIN *Falco columbarius (b?,w)*
F   1 with prey Skinflats 2 Jan & 1 on 23 Feb (AB GO). Kinneil: 1 on 25 Jan & 28 Mar; 1 caught a Dunlin on 16 Oct & 1 Nov but on last date lost it to two crows (GO JF DT). M Blackness 22 Oct (AS).
S   In summer, pair Touch & M Glen Ogle (DOE). 1 Sheriffmuir 8 Feb; M Stronend 25 Sep; 1 Braeleny 20 Oct (RC DOE DJC). Attending finch flock at Cromlix: F on 3 & 5 Jan, M &/or F 1 Nov to 20 Dec (MVB).

PEREGRINE *Falco peregrinus (B,W)*
F   Six coastal records Feb & Aug-Nov, 1 Kinneil 14 Jun was odd date (DT). Inland singles at Falkirk 22 Feb & Denny on 23rd, R.Carron on 21 Sep (stooped at Blackheaded Gull on ground), Slamannan on 15 Nov (MA WRB).
C   2 territories checked, 2 pairs were successful rearing 4Y (PSA).
S   20 territories checked, 11 pairs + 2 apparent singles, 8 successful pairs of which 6 reared 15Y (PSA). Seen on carse Jan, Mar, Dec (WRB DT TJ DR).

RED GROUSE *Lagopus lagopus (B,W)*
       Generally under-recorded
F   2 Darnrig Moss 4 Mar (MA).
S   In spring at Kippen Muir (4),Earlsburn (8), Cock Hill (6), (DAC CJH DT). Frequent in summer on Eildreach plateau, Glen Ogle (DOE). 4 Sheriffmuir 13 Jan & 10 on 18 Sep (AD CJH). 7 Glen Lochay 12 Oct (PWS). 3 Breac-nic ridge, L.Lubnaig 23 Nov (DJC).

PTARMIGAN *Lagopus mutus (b,w)*
       No records received

*BLACK GROUSE *Tetrao tetrix (B,W)*
       There are clearly leks that are not being visited.
S   11 (7M) Braeleny 23 Oct & 18M (+4 at 3km NE) on 12 Dec. Single M

L.Katrine, Hart Hill 5 Apr (dead), Stronend 4 Aug, Carron Valley Res 15 Nov. F+4Y Braeval 3 Jul, 10 Glen Finglas 31 Oct (DJC DOE DT DAC).

GREY PARTRIDGE *Perdix perdix (B,W)*

F   6 Skinflats 7 Feb, 26 on 30 Oct & 29 on 2 Nov (GO DT). 12 Grangemouth 14 Dec (DMB). 21 Kinneil 25 Jan,10 on 1 Dec & 7 on 29th (GO CJH). 10 Camelon 6 Jan (MA).

C   23 Menstrie 2 Jan & 19 on 19 Oct (BRT PMA). 3 AoT on Devon WBS (CJH).

S   12 Thornhill Carse 9 Feb &13 on 2 Nov (DAC DOE). 9 Hill of Row 15 Jan (RC). 8 Lecropt 22 Nov (RJ). 38 Forthbank 15 Dec & 15 Cambuskenneth on 5th (AT RC). 10 Earlsburn 1 Nov (DOE).

*QUAIL *Coturnix coturnix (b)*

S   3M calling W of Thornhill 16 Jun & F+11Y seen 4 Aug (SS). M E of Thornhill on 30 Jul & 3 on 31st. 3 M Drip Carse 14 Jul (P Hancock WRB). 2 M Thornhill Carse (Frew) 19 Jul & 1 on 12 Aug (DR).

PHEASANT *Phasianus colchicus (B,W)*

      Abundant (usually by releases) on fields next to keepered estates.

C   Probably only 2 AoT on Devon WBS (approx. 1 km sq) (CJH).

S   13 AoT per km sq on Doune CBC- 64 % of 1996 (NB). Albino Dunblane 6 Jan (RB).

*WATER RAIL *Rallus aquaticus (w)*

F   Kinneil: 1 on 22 Feb & 24 Sep 6 Sep (BDA GO). Skinflats: 2 on 2 Aug & 25-29 Sep, 1 on 21 Oct (AB GO).

C   Cambus Pools: 1 on 19 Jul, then 1 or 2 to 22 Dec. 1 Gartmorn 17 Mar. 1 Tullibody Inch 2 Oct. (CJH WRB MC)

S   2 Hutchinson Dam 21 Sep; 1 L.Watston 13 Nov (WRB CJH).

MOORHEN *Gallinula chloropus (B,W)*

F   18 Kinneil 23 Feb, nest 11 May. Pair +2Y Skinflats 6 Aug, 12 on 4 Dec. (GO AB). Max on Union Canal at Brightons 24 on 9 Mar & 38 on 16 Nov (JW). Max on Forth/Clyde Canal 13 on 9 Feb & 20 on 20 Dec (DM).

C   3 AoT Cambus in Jun, max 15 on 20 Sep (CJH WRB). 3 AoT on Devon WBS (CJH).

S   Airthrey: 23 on 3 Jan, 12 on 14 Dec. 9 Cambuskenneth 12 Jan & 7 on 9 Feb, 10 on 10 Nov (AT MK). 2 pair Ashfield Ponds 4 Apr (WRB). 2 pair bred Torrie Lochan (BWB). 4Y Gartmore 11 May (DAC). At Killin marshes from 22 Apr, 1Y seen 26 Aug (PWS). Max 7 at river roost Callander in Jan, only 2 in Dec (DJC).

COOT *Fulica atra (B,W)*

      WEBS peak in Dec was 11x the Sep count, implying heavy immigration (NB).

F   1 nest Kinneil. Returned to Skinflats 8 Feb, Pair + 1Y 15 Jun (AB GO).

C   34 suddenly appeared on floods at Cambus 16 Mar, + 9 to E of

Devonmouth on 22nd; only 3 AoT on pools in Jun (WRB CJH). 620 Gartmorn 15 Jan to 110 on 17 Mar; 250 on 25 Oct to 810 on 26 Dec (MC DOE).

S   Airthrey: 29 on 9 Mar, 46 on 16 Nov (AT MK). 297 Lake of Menteith 29 Jan, 21 on 26 Sep to 140 on 29 Dec (NB). 17 L.Watston 18 Mar (CJH). 40 Cambusmore 1 Aug (PWS). 1 nest Torrie Lochan (BWB).

OYSTERCATCHER *Haematopus ostralegus (B,W)*

101 on Forth estuary Feb (DMB).

Spring return inland in Feb: Ashfield 8th, 2 Airthrey 12th, over Stirling 17th, 4 L.Dochart 18th, Kippen 22nd; also 500 Craigforth 22nd & 23rd (WRB MVB DT DAC NB).

F   140 Blackness 27 Oct. Kinneil: 60 on 8 Apr, 105 on 30 Aug, partial albino present 23 Jan (DT DMB CJH). 46 Skinflats 2 Nov & 15 on 15 Jun (MVB AB). 72 Higgins Neuk 25 Feb (DSF).

C   50 on Cambus floods 17 Mar. 9 AoT Devon WBS, as 1997 (CJH).

S   25 Killin 2 Mar & 100 Cambusmore GP on 4th; 171 by Forth, Gargunnock-Kippen, on 10th; 305 Blairdrummond 17th; 122 Ashfield on 23rd (PWS MT NB MW).

Breeding pairs: 6 Braes Doune (Severie),10 Glen Finglas, 2 Lake of Menteith, 10 per sq km Doune CBC (DOE NB).

*LITTLE RINGED PLOVER *Charadrius dubius*

S   1 on Allan Water above Kinbuck 7 Jun, absence of wingbar & typical call noted (WRB). *Only second record for area, Ed.*

RINGED PLOVER *Charadrius hiaticula (b,W)*

F   Pair Grangemouth 29 Jun. 1st of autumn Skinflats 2 Jul & 35 on 16 Aug. 43 Kinneil 14 Aug. 20 Blackness 3 Aug. 64 Bo'ness 31 Dec.(GO DMB AS).

S   Pair Barbush GP 16 Mar, 2Y on 28 May (WRB). 1 Killin Marshes 22 Apr, 14 & 29 Jul (PWS).

GOLDEN PLOVER Pluvialis apricaria (B,W)

The small number of likely breeding records may indicate a reduction in range compared with twenty years ago. Inland passage in spring negligible, numbers high but localised by estuary in late October.

F   15 Blackness 3 Aug, 850 on 22 Oct & 280 on 27th (AB AS CJH). Skinflats: 1st on 14 Jul & 20 on 15th, 147 on 2 Nov & 120 on 14 Dec (GO MVB). 80 Kinneil 23 Nov. 572 Higgins Neuk 25 Oct, 182 on 28 Dec (DSF).

C   1 Ben Cleuch 31 May (DMB).

S   3 Glen Lochay (Meall nan Subh) 16 Jul (WRB). 20 Lecropt 4 Oct (DT). 41 Braes of Doune 23 Nov (DOE).

GREY PLOVER *Pluvialis squatarola (W)*

F   Few on estuary this year. 12 Kinneil 9 Feb; 1 Kinneil & 3 Higgins Neuk on 6 Sep. Skinflats: 1 on 21 May; 1st of autumn 2 on 6 Aug, max 5 on 1 Sep (DMB BDA DSF GO AB).

LAPWING   *Vanellus vanellus (B,W)*
2509 Forth estuary in Dec (DMB).
F   Skinflats: 720 on 9 Feb; 65 on 9 Jul to 400 on 3 Aug, 1505 on 2 Nov & 1220 on 14 Dec. Kinneil: 450 on 2 Jan; 65 on 29 Jun, 600 on 26 Sep & 1000 on 30 Nov (MVB DT DMB). 224 Higgins Neuk 26 Jan, 201 on 6 Sep & 1400 on 15 Nov (DSF).
C   3 AoT Cambus 28 Mar but only 1 by 3 Jun. 19 AoT Devon WBS (WRB CJH). 416 Cambus 8 Aug (DSF).
S   Spring return to Ashfield 10 Feb, 16 AoT Kinbuck 5 Apr (WRB). 7 pairs/ sq km Doune CBC, x1.5 1996 (NB). 60 Cambusmore 4 Mar, 2 AoT Killin on 6th (PWS). 20 AoT Braes of Doune (Severie) 12 May (DOE). 600 Lecropt on 11 Sep & 800 on 30th (DOE LJM). 300 Cambuskenneth 10 Nov (AT).

KNOT   *Calidris canutus (W)*
5380 Forth Estuary in Jan (DMB).
F   3000 Bo'ness 31 Dec (AS). Kinneil: 5200 on 23 Jan; 1 on 16 Jul, 33 on 7 Sep, 1000 on 18 Nov & 1400 on 29 Dec. Skinflats: 800 on 11 Jan; 1 on 15 Jul, 17 on 20 Sep (CJH GO DT AB MVB). 32 Higgins Neuk 26 Jan (DSF).

SANDERLING   *Calidris alba (p)*
F   5 Kinneil 29 Jul, 4 on 17 Aug & 2 on 3 Sep (GO DT DSF).

*LITTLE STINT   *Calidris minuta (p)*
F   1 Kinneil 10 & 12 Aug (DT). 1 juv Skinflats 1 to 4 Sep (GO AB).

CURLEW SANDPIPER   *Calidris ferruginea (p)*
F   1st Kinneil 2 (adults) on 17 Aug to 2 on 3 Sep (DT DSF). 5 Skinflats 1 Sep, max 11 on 3rd, last 2 on 17th, all juvs (GO AB).
Area Summary (half monthly)

Aug	Sep
0 2	13 4

DUNLIN   *Calidris alpina (b?,W)*
7644 Forth Estuary Dec (DMB).
F   Kinneil: 3600 on 29 Feb; 120 on 3 Aug & 350 on 30th, 1000 on 1 Nov, 6000 on 13 Dec (DMB DT CJH). Skinflats: 3120 on 11 Jan & 2850 on 9 Feb; 2500 on 2 Nov & 1600 on 14 Dec (MVB). 1545 Higgins Neuk 26 Jan, 12 on 2 Aug & 320 on 30 Nov (DSF).
S   Pair + 2 singles Glen Ogle (Eildreach peat hags) in summer (DOE). 1 Killin 29 Jul (PWS).

RUFF   *Philomachus pugnax (p)*
F   1st Skinflats 2 Aug, max 15 on 30th & 14 on 1-2 Sep, last 4 on 19th (AB GO BDA). Kinneil: 1 on 28 Mar & 14 Apr; 1st of autumn 30 Aug, max 3 on 6 Sep, last 1 on 26th (DT GO DMB BDA).
C   3 Tullibody Inch 11 Oct (DMB).
Area Summary (half monthly)

Mar	Apr	Aug	Sep	Oct
0 1	1 0	1 17	17 8	3 0

JACK SNIPE Lymnocryptes minimus (w)
F	1 Grangemouth 12 Jan. 1 Kinneil 2 Jan & 22 Feb, 3 on 28 Mar, 4 on 1 Nov & 5 on 1 Dec (DMB BDA DT GO).
C	1 Alva Moss 22 May (MA). *A remarkable date and place which repeats one seen in spring 1987 by a NCC survey team (Ed).*
S	1 Ashfield 1 Dec (WRB).

SNIPE *Gallinago gallinago (B,W)*
Probably under-recorded in breeding season but may have decreased (Ed).
F	28 Grangemouth 11 Jan (DMB). Max Kinneil 6 on 25 Jan, 17 on 3 Aug & 20 on 1 Dec .1st Skinflats 31 Jul & max only 9 on 25 Sep (GO DT). 10 Larbert (R.Carron) 21 Oct (MA).
C	15 Cambus Pools 19 Jul & 38 on 9 Aug (CJH WRB). 32 Gartmorn Dam 20 Oct (MC).
S	Drumming in Apr-May at Kippen Muir, Glen Finglas, Severie (3) (DAC DOE). 1 Glen Buckie 5 May, 3 Inverlochlarig 18 Jul & 1 L.Dhu (Rusky) on 29th (DT AT). 1 Killin Marshes 18 Jun to 18 Jul (PWS). Autumn numbers not above 5.

WOODCOCK *Scolopax rusticola (B,W)*
Under-recorded (Ed).
F/S	Roding or in breeding season at: L.Ard, Blairdrummond, Dunblane, Pendreich (BoA), North Third Res (DOE AT MVB BDA). 1 L.Dhu (Rusky) 2 Dec (DJC).
F	1 Skinflats 31 Jan (GO), 1 Kinneil 28 Mar (DT).

BLACK-TAILED GODWIT *Limosa limosa (W)*
F	Kinneil was the major site with Skinflats being significant only in May and late Sep to Nov, site max was 92 Kinneil 16 Nov (GO et al). The spring decline here fits with fresh records at other sites. After very few in late May to early July, numbers built up to an autumn plateau of around 65 by early Sep. The high area total in November is probably due to double counting of birds commuting from Kinneil to Skinflats.
C	29 Alloa Inch 4 May (DMB).
S	5 at Killin on 28 Apr (PWS). *NB similarity in date to birds found dead in Glen Lochay in 1996 (Ed).*

Area Summary (half monthly)

	Jan	Feb	Mar	Apr	May	Jun	Jul	Aug	Sep	Oct	Nov	Dec
Knnl	68 60	84 58	61 59	60 45	30 2	12 2	6 21	32 20	51 42	25 42	8 92	54 57
Skn					9 11		4 7	6	7 28	30 28	17 40	3
Area	68 60	84 58	61 59	60 50	68 13	13 2	10 28	32 26	58 70	55 70	101 132	60 47

BAR-TAILED GODWIT *Limosa lapponica (W)*
301 Forth Estuary Feb (DMB).
F	Kinneil: 285 on 11 Jan, 300 on 9 Feb, last 2 on 13 Apr; lst of autumn 1 on 9 Jul, 55 on 1 Nov, 160 on 29 Dec (DMB AB DT CJH). 6 Skinflats 4 Jul (GO).

WHIMBREL *Numenius phaeopus (p)*
F   1 ->W Skinflats 23 Apr, 4 on 11 May (GO AB), 1 Kincardine Bridge
       17 May (DSF). 1st of autumn, 2 Skinflats 8 Jul, max 7 Skinflats 5 Aug &
       7 Kinneil on 17th, last 1 Skinflats 18 Sep. (GO DT).
C   1 R.Devon (Alva) 15 May (CJH). 1 Alloa Inch 14 Jun (DMB).1 Cambus
       8 Aug (DSF).
S   4 L.Mahaick 12 May (DOE).
       Area Summary (half monthly)

May	Jun	Jul	Aug	Sep
10 1	1 0	4 4	10 8	3 1

CURLEW *Numenius arquata (B,W)*
       The March return is clear in inland records, and early return to estuary. Also
       contrast in breeding populations E & W of Callander (Ed).
       906 Forth estuary Sep (DMB).
F   181 Skinflats 9 Feb, 69 Higgins Neuk on 26th (DSF MVB). Kinneil: 200
       on 6 Jul, 440 on 16 Aug (AB DMB). Skinflats: 100 on 5 Aug; 374 on
       14 Dec (AB MVB). 78 Higgins Neuk 19 Jul & 228 on 2 Aug (DSF).
       Inland in winter: 78 Polmont 28 Dec (JW).
C   29 R.Devon Dollar 22 Mar (RN). 2 AoT Devon WBS (CJH). 65 Cambus
       12 Jan, 42 on 27 Dec (CJH BRT).
S   20 Thornhill Carse 1 Mar, 25 Kippen Muir on 4th & 70 on 5th; 40
       Lecropt 15 Mar (DT DAC). 1 AoT on Doune CBC (NB). Frequent on
       Sheriffmuir 30 Mar & Glen a'Chroin (Callander) 30 May (AT CJH). On
       Braes of Doune, 12 May, 15 pr Drumloist, 25 pr Severie & 4 pr
       Buchany. 1 pr Glen Finglas 13 Apr (DOE).

SPOTTED REDSHANK *Tringa erythropus (p)*
F   1 Skinflats 19 Jan to 6 Mar; 28 Aug & 19 Sep (AD AB GO BDA). Kinneil:
       1 from 11 Jan to 15 Apr (changed to BP); 2 on 27 Apr, 1 on 28 May. 1 or
       2 from 16 Jul to 30 Sep, 1 from 1 Nov to 20 Dec (GO DT et al).
C   2 Cambus Pools 9 Sep (CJH).
       Area Total (half monthly)

Jan	Feb	Mar	Apr	May	-	Jul	Aug	Sep	Oct	Nov	Dec
1 1	0 1	2 1	1 2	0 1		0 1	0 3	4 4	0 0	1 1	1 1

REDSHANK *Tringa totanus (B,W)*
       1967 Forth Estuary Sep (DMB).
F   Skinflats: 590 on 9 Feb; 100 at pools 6 Aug, 740 on 2 Nov (MVB AB).
       Kinneil: 400 on 18 Apr; 350 on 28 Jul, 750 on 12 Aug,1270 on 14 Sep,
       1175 on 14 Dec. (DT DMB). 140 Higgins Neuk 25 Feb; 48 on 2 Aug, 156
       on 30 Nov(DSF).
C   6 Cambus floods 16 Mar, none bred (WRB CJH). 3 on R.Devon 11 Mar
       (NB), 3 AoT Devon WBS (CJH).
S   6 Kippen Muir 23 Mar (DAC). 7 on Forth at Stirling 10 Mar (AT). 1
       Ashfield 19 Jan (MW). 5 AoT Kinbuck 5 Apr; 28 nearby 7 Jun (WRB).

GREENSHANK *Tringa nebularia (p)*
F   Skinflats: 1 on 3 to 11 May, 2 on 12th; 1 on 9 Jul, regular from 20 Aug
       to 29 Sep, max 8 on 2 Sep, last 3 on 11 Oct. 1 Carronshore 8 Jul. 1

Kinneil 28 Jun & 6 Jul, max 11 on 9 Aug, last 2 on 1 Nov (GO AB DT CKM).

C   2 Cambus Pools 16 Aug & 9 Sep – left high to S (DAC CJH). 1 Alloa Inch 2 Oct (CJH).1 Dollar 5 Oct (RN).

S   1 Lake of Menteith 11 Apr & 1 Killin on 19th (DOE PWS). 1 Cocksburn Res 6 Aug (JMi) & 1 Ashfield on 19th (WRB). 1 Carron Valley Res 6 Sep (RKP).

Area Summary (half monthly)

Apr	May	Jun	Jul	Aug	Sep	Oct	Nov
2 1	2 0	0 1	3 0	19 15	17 9	5 1	1 0

*GREEN SANDPIPER *Tringa ochropus (p)*

F   1 Skinflats 30 Aug to 2 Sep, 2 on 4th (AB GO DT). 1 Lathallan Pool 28 & 31 Dec (JW).

S   1 Carron Valley Res 30 Oct (RKP).

COMMON SANDPIPER *Tringa hypoleucos (B)*

Spring return: 3 Devon WBS 12 Apr, 1 Doune Ponds 15th, 1 Barbush on 16th, 1 L.Venachar on 19th & widespread thereafter (CJH DOE WRB DAC).

F   1 R.Carron at Camelon 23 May (MA -? *breeding, Ed*). Kinneil: 3 Jul to 11 Sep, max 10 on 30 Jul & 17 on 21 Aug. Skinflats: max 3 from 2 Jul to 6 Aug (GO DT AB). 6 Higgins Neuk 19 Jul (DSF).

C   6 AoT on Devon WBS. 1st of autumn Tullibody Inch 7 Jul (CJH).

S   1 AoT Doune CBC (NB).

Estuary autumn totals :

	Jul	Aug	Sep
	4 19	10 17	6 0

TURNSTONE *Arenaria interpres (W)*

3 Kinneil 12 & 19 Aug (DT). 7 Blackness 21 Mar & 6 on 31 Jul, 4 Carriden 14 Dec (GO DMB).

ARCTIC SKUA *Stercorarius parasiticus (p)*

F   Grangemouth area: 3 on 17 Aug & 20 Sep, 4 on 17 Sep & 11 Oct & 1 on 2 Nov (DT AJC).

*GREAT SKUA *Stercorarius skua (p)*

F   1 Kinneil 12 Sep (A Paton L Monty).

*LITTLE GULL *Larus minutus (p).*

F   1, 1st S, Skinflats 9 May (HMD). 3, 1st W, Kinneil 17 Aug (DT).

BLACK-HEADED GULL *Larus ridibundus (B,W)*

70 Skinflats 23 Jun with 1st juv 2 Jul (AB GO). 3300 Airth (roost) 22 Nov (CJH). 400 Higgins Neuk 25 Feb & 250 on 28 Dec (DSF).

C   600 Cambus floods 15 Mar (WRB). 1300 Alloa Inch 2 Oct, 1100 Tullibody Inch 19 Nov (CJH). At Alva 500 following plough 13 Aug; 912 on 24 Dec (CJH NB).

S   500 Craigforth 9 Feb (AT).180 pairs at Ashfield colony in Apr, only 16 pairs in May after disturbance – reared 20Y. 380 Hutchison Dam 15 Mar (WRB). 80 at Thornhill colony 27 Apr (DOE). Only 1 at Cambusmore 6 Apr (CJH). 1385 Gogar 24 Dec (NB).

COMMON GULL *Larus canus* *(B,W)*
F   400 Higgins Neuk 25 Feb (DSF). 610 Black Loch 4 Sep; 424 Slamannan
     4 Mar & 543 on 11 Nov (NB).
S   461 Drymen 15 Jan & 1026 on 11 Mar (NB). 600 Cambusmore GP
     4 Mar, only 72 by 6 Apr (PWS CJH). 600 Killin 5&6 Mar, 40 (10 nests)
     Breachlaich Res 29 May (PWS).

LESSER BLACK-BACKED GULL *Larus fuscus (b,S)0*
     Few mid-winter records, as usual; increasing nest attempts on roofs;
     more stayed late into autumn.
F   1 Skinflats 22 Feb, 8 on 27 Dec (GO). 4 Larbert 9 Feb & 6 L.Ellrig on
     19th (NB-maybe start of spring return, Ed). 3 (1 Pr) Carronmouth
     cairns 29 Jun (DMB).
C   54 AoT on Menstrie bond roofs 9 Apr (CJH). 100 around Cambus bond
     in Apr (WRB).
S   1 Arnprior 5 Jan, 1 L.Coulter 14 Jan, 2 Killin on 23rd; 2 Carron Valley
     Res 14 Dec & 5 R.Forth on 16th (DAC NB PWS WME AT). 500 Fallin
     tip 24 Aug, on carse of Stirling 400 on 23 Sep, 144 on 21 Oct, 5 on 5 Nov
     (WRB MT CJH).

HERRING GULL *Larus argentatus (b?,S,W)*
F   4600 Kinneil 29 Dec (CJH). 1200 Higgins Neuk 25 Feb & 1274 on
     29 May (DSF).
C   2 AoT Menstrie bond roofs 9 Apr (CJH). Nest attempts on roof of
     Cambus bond in May (WRB).
S   2000 on Fallin tip 24 Aug. Roosting Cambus-Tullibody Inch: 1700 on
     28 Aug, & 3400 on 19 Nov (WRB CJH).

ICELAND GULL *Larus glaucoides*
F   1 (imm, prob. 2nd W) Kinneil 5 Jan (CKM).

GREAT BLACK-BACKED GULL *Larus marinus (S,W)*
     Highly under-reported (Ed).
F   100 Kinneil 8 Oct (CKM). 27 Higgins Neuk 19 Jul (DSF). 20 L.Ellrig
     5 Jan & 10 on 15 Oct (MA NB). 87 Black Loch 5 Jan (MA – v.high inland
     count, Ed)
S   20 Buchlyvie 11 Mar (NB).

KITTIWAKE *Rissa tridactyla (P,w)*
F   Skinflats (estuary) 160 left high to E on 2 Nov. 1 ad Kinneil 25 Jul (DT).

SANDWICH TERN *Sterna sandvicensis (P)*
F   440 Blackness 31 Jul & 350 on 3 Aug (GO AB). 200 Carriden 23 Sep
     (DMB). 78 Kinneil 11 Sep, last 5 on 10 Oct (GO DT). 71 Higgins Neuk
     6 Sep (DSF).

COMMON TERN *Sterna hirundo (B)*
F   lst, 5 Kinneil 4 May (DT). 125 pairs Grangemouth Docks 10 Jun (DMB).
     34 Skinflats 12 Aug flying high W (GO). 12 Higgins Neuk 6 Sep (DSF).

*ARCTIC TERN *Sterna paradisaea*
F   2 Higgins Neuk 6 Sep (DSF).

*GUILLEMOT *Uria aalge (W)*
F   2 Kinneil 19 Sep & 1 Skinflats on 29th (AJC GO).

FERAL PIGEON *Columba livia*
F   80 Bo'ness 27 Oct (CJH).
C   40 Menstrie in Dec (BRT). 500 Tullibody 31 Oct. 200 Stirling 4 Nov (NB).

STOCK DOVE *Columba oenas (B,W)*
Widespread in small numbers, surely much overlooked though BBS records only in farmland, 0.2 per 10 km (Ed)
F   36 by R.Carron at Larbert 4 Nov (MA). Max 7 Skinflats Feb-Sep (DT GO).
C   Probably 1 AoT on Devon WBS (CJH). 17 Cambus 29 Sep (WRB).

WOODPIGEON *Columba palumba (B,W)*
    Greatly underreported. BBS shows 48 per 10 km on farmland, 3x more than urban or conifer habitats (NB).
F   1900 on brassicas Kinneil 4 Jan (MVB). 100 Skinflats 27 Dec (AB).
C   Max on Devon WBS 21 on 3 Apr (CJH).
S   7 AoT per km sq on Doune CBC (NB). 750 Lecropt 15 Mar (DT). 18 ->S L.Lubnaig 4 Nov (CJH).

COLLARED DOVE *Streptopelia decaocto (B,W)*
    Under-reported, but scarce away from suburbs and large farms (Ed)
F   Vagrant to Skinflats, 2 on 31 Aug &12 Sep (GO).
C   46 Menstrie on 13 Dec & 44 on 31st (PMA BRT).
    1 pair on Doune CBC (NB). 1 Killin 5 Apr & 10 Jun. 4 Glen Dochart (Ledcharrie) 4 Jun (PWS).

CUCKOO *Cuculus canorus (B)*
    1st records at Balquhidder on 4 May, Cambushinnie on 11th, Killin on 14th & North Third Res on 15th (DOE AT PWS BDA).
BBS shows 8 per 10 km on farmland, 2 in conifers and 3 at moor/conifer edge (NB).

BARN OWL *Tyto alba (b,w)*
S   Regular Thornhill Carse Feb to Dec (DR). 1 at Thornhill, Lecropt & Stirling in Jan-Feb (SS JW WRB). Noted Killin, Callander, Doune, Dunblane (dead), Blairdrummond, Craigforth, L.Watston, Forthbank (PWS DJC SS GO DOE LKM WRB AT).

TAWNY OWL *Strix aluco (B,W)*.
C   Reported Menstrie, Alva (BRT PMA).
S   Reported Killin, Balquhidder, Aberfoyle, Lake of Menteith, W Flanders Moss, Stirling, Buchlyvie (PWS BDA DOE DT DAC).

*LONG-EARED OWL *Asio otus (b,w)*
F   2 Ad +2Y Skinflats 5 -26 May (GO BDA AB)
C   1 Cambus 22 Jun (PMA).
S   .2Y heard Drip Carse14 Jul (WRB). Seen hunting Thornhill Carse (Frew) Jun & Jul, Y heard from 4 Aug with 3 on 12th, 1 on 23 Sep (DR MT).

SHORT-EARED OWL *Asio flammeus (b,W)*
F   Kinneil: 1 on 18 Jan, 1 on 9 Feb & 3 on 22nd to 28 Apr, 1 on 10 Nov. 1 Skinflats 15 & 22 Feb (AS GO BDA DT).
S   1 Cringate Muir 26 Jun (GO). 1 Carron Valley Forest 1 Aug (RKP). 1 Invertrossachs 17 Jul (DOE). 1 Braeleny 30 May (CJH). 1 Thornhill Carse 8 Jan & 6 Mar (DR). 2 Thornhill 2 Oct (SS).

SWIFT *Apus apus (B)*
1st records: Stirling (10) & Buchlyvie on 5 May, Dunblane on 6th, Airthrey on 7th, Alva on 9th, Ashfield on 10th (DT DAC NB DMB PMA). Last August records Dunblane on 7th, Ashfield & Killin (30) on 8th, Alva & Kinneil on 12th, BoA on 13th, Stirling on 28th (NB WRB PMS PMA DT CJH). 2 Cambusbarron 6 Sep (DAC).
F   150 over Kinneil woods 14 Jun (DT).
S   Arrival at Killin 18 May (PWS). Max in July: 55 BoA 24th (CJH), 30 Dunblane 26th (NB). 45 BoA 3 Aug circled round a Sparrowhawk, the single Swift at Stirling on 28th was chased by one (CJH DT).

KINGFISHER *Alcedo atthis (b,w)*
F   1 Skinflats 18 Jan & 2 on 2 Nov; 1 Kinneil 23 Nov to 26 Dec (GO MVB DSF DT M&JC). 1 on Avon at Grangemouth 23 & 25 Sep (AS). 1 on Union Canal at Maddiston 14 Dec (JW). 2 pairs on Carron at Larbert all year, one burrow seen & two broods (5J) in Jun (MA).
C   2 on Devon at Alva 10 Sep (GEL). 1 Tullibody 25 Oct (WRB).
S   1 Killin 15 Sep (PWS). 3 Balquhidder 9 Jul. 1 L.Lubnaig 15 Sep & 28 Nov. 1 Callander 9 Feb, 26 Aug, 21 Oct (WRB DOE DJC D Warnock DAC). 1 Sheriffmuir 8 Feb & on R.Allan at BoA 23 Aug (BB CJH); at Ashfield 14 Feb & 9 Sep (WRB). 1 Stirling 16 Dec (AT).

GREEN WOODPECKER *Picus viridis (B,W)*
F   1 Torwood 7 Apr (AB).
C   2 AoT Menstrie in Apr (CJH).
S   In spring/summer many reports from L.Ard Forest (2AoT) through Callander to BoA; also North Third Res, Plean CP.

GREAT SPOTTED WOODPECKER *Dendrocopus major (B,W)*
F   F+Juv Falkirk in Jul & Aug (JW). M Larbert in Jan/Feb. 1 Denny 4 Jan & Fankerton on 5th, Bonnybridge on 19 Nov (DT MA MC). M Skinflats 15 Feb , 23 Oct to 3 Dec (GO).
C   Through year at Alva, Juv in Jul-Aug (PMA). 1 on Devon WBS 25 May was 1st in 3 years (CJH).
In spring/summer many reports from L.Ard Forest through Callander to BoA; also Plean CP.

SKYLARK *Alauda arvensis (B,W)*
F   280 Kinneil 2 Jan (DT). Singing Skinflats 6 Mar, Higgins Neuk on 18th (AB DSF).
C   11 AoT on Devon WBS (CJH).
S   9 AoT per sq Km on Doune CBC, x2.5 1996 (NB). Widespread and frequent Braeleny-A'Chroin 30 May (CJH). Song Cambuskenneth 9 Feb. 30 Kippen 9 Mar, 34 Forthbank 15 Dec (HK AT). 40 ->W Lecropt 4 Oct & 50 ->SW on 17th. 10 ->S BoA 7 Oct (DT CJH). 60 Thornhill Carse 2 Nov & 102 (2nd site) on 8th (DOE SS).

SAND MARTIN *Riparia riparia (B)*
     1st records: 15 Lake of Menteith & 1 Airthrey 3 Apr, 1 Skinflats & 20 L.Voil on 12th, 13 Barbush on 13th, 12 BoA on 16th (DOE MVB DAC WRB AT). Last 4 Ashfield 4 Sep, some Cambus on 5th (WRB CJH).
F   31 -> E Skinflats 15 Aug (GO).
C   Probably over 100 in huge Swallow flock at Cambus 28 Aug (CJH)
S   200 L.Dochart 20 May (PWS). 35 nests Inverlochlarig 15 Jul (WRB).

SWALLOW *Hirundo rustica (B)*
1st records: Falkirk on 7 & 9 Apr, Skinflats & Lake of Menteith on 11th, Doune, Strathyre & Killin on 12th, BoA & Carron Valley Res on 13th, Alva & Buchlyvie on 14th. Last in late October: Larbert, Gargunnock & Stronend on 21st, Falkirk on 22nd, Airthrey on 24th, Callander on 25th, Blackness (6) on 27th, Alva on 28th (MA GO DOE DAC PWS DMB CJH PMA DJC).
F   12->W Kinneil 27 Apr & 100->W on 25 Aug (DT).
C   Immense roost in Forth reedbed upstream of Cambus, assembling after sunset: 13,000 on 28 Aug & 14,000 on 31st, 13,500 on 5 Sep (CJH).
S   7 AoT per sq km on Doune CBC, as 1996 (NB). 200 at roost Doune Ponds 6 Aug, 300 on 30th & 1000 on 15 Sep (DOE).

HOUSE MARTIN *Delichon urbica (B)*
     1st records: 5 BoA 16 Apr, 3 L.Venachar on 19th, Carronshore on 22nd ; next reported were 3 Airth 4 May, Skinflats on 5th, Doune on 6th & Lake of Menteith on 7th; arrived Killin 14 May (AT DAC AB DT GO NB DOE PWS).
     Early departure, last 120 Dunblane 26 Sep (MVB)
S   3 nests per sq km on Doune CBC, 20 % of 1994-5 average (NB). 12 nests Ashfield, increase (WRB).

TREE PIPIT *Anthus trivialis (B)*
     1st records: 3 in song Aberfoyle on 27 Apr, 1 L.Katrine on 30th, 2 Rhuveag on 5 May (BDA DAC DT).
S   6 Glen Lochay 16 Jul (WRB), still in L.Ard Forest 12 Aug (CJH).

MEADOW PIPIT *Anthus pratensis (B,W)*
     BBS shows 93 per 10 km in moor/conifer edge, 73 on moorland,13 in conifers & 0.4 on farmland.
F   Song Skinflats 23 Mar, 20 on 11 Apr; 60 on 20 Sep (AB DT).
     On lower Devon to 12 Apr, return 13 Aug (CJH).

S   Return to Cock Hill 6 Mar (CJH). 20 Killin 2 Apr, 100 on 4 Sep (PWS). 13 in 70 min Ben Bhreac (L.Ard Forest) 23 May, frequent Braeleny - A'Chroin on 30th. 250 Sheriffmuir 30 Aug, still frequent 18 Sep (MVB CJH).

ROCK PIPIT *Anthus petrosus (w)*

F   Kinneil: 1 on 2nd Jan & 2 on 11th; 1 on 1 & 30 Nov (DT GO DMB). 1 Blackness 18 Oct (CJH).

GREY WAGTAIL *Motacilla cinerea (B,w)*

      Winter records Jan-Feb: R.Devon, Alva; Nov-Dec: Gart, R.Devon, Alva, Cocksburn Res, Manorneuk, R.Carron (Larbert, 6 on 15 Dec) Forth-Clyde Canal (GEL PMA AT MA NB DM).

      Average breeding population, after poor 1996 (HR). 1 pair Doune CBC (NB). Summer records at 8 sites Trossachs (1st juv seen 10 May) & Hillfoots (DAC AT). Pair on R.Avon, Grangemouth, 6 Apr (AS).

PIED WAGTAIL *Motacilla alba (B, w)*

F   5 Grangemouth 17 Jan (AT). White Wagtails M.a.alba : 1 Glen Finglas 13 Apr (DOE).

C   3 AoT on Devon WBS (CJH).

S   5 inland records in Jan-Feb, Buchlyvie-Stirling (DAC AT). 5 AoT per sq km Doune CBC, 1st juv seen 4 Jun (NB). 28 Barbush 10 Sep, 14 Buchlyvie 16 Nov (WRB DAC).

WAXWING *Bombycilla garrulus*

F   8 Aberfoyle 29 Jan to 16 Feb (DOE DAC). 1 Stirling 10 & 28 Jan, then 50 St Ninians 12 Feb (DSF) & 25 nearby 16th to 21st (DAC); 27 Springkerse 22 & 23 Feb (DT GO).

DIPPER *Cinclus cinclus (B,W)*

      The WEBS data total 23 records for January but only 3 in February and 1 in March (NB), this shows an early spring departure to breeding territories though many of them are occupied through the winter (DAC AD DJC); note that some records are from lower stretches of Devon & Allan where Dippers do not breed (Ed). In Dec at least 19 on 3 river sections of WEBS circuit.

F   2 in Apr & Sep on R.Avon at Birkhill, 2 km above tidal limit (AS). ? Lowest breeding pair on Avon (Ed). 3 pairs in Jan on Carron (MA – about 4 km above tidal limit).

S   1 pair on Doune CBC, 1st juv seen 7 May (NB). Average site occupancy in Trossachs (HR). Nested in outflow pipe of L.Katrine weir (DAC).

WREN *Troglodytes troglodytes (B,W)*

      Under-recorded (Ed). BBS shows 42 per 10 km in conifers, 19 on farmland & 11 in 'Urban'.

C   11 AoT on 5 Km of lower Devon, much as 1996 (CJH).

      3 AoT per sq Km Doune CBC (NB). In Dec still at head of Gleann an Dubh Corrie (DJC). In Mine Wood on 1 Dec 2M were countersinging in dark, 40 min after sunset (AT).

HEDGE SPARROW *Accentor modularis (B,W)*
Under-recorded (Ed).BBS shows 11 per 10 km in 'Urban', 10 in moor/conifer edge, 4 in conifers & 3 in farmland.
C   5 AoT on 5 km of lower Devon, much as 1996 (CJH).
S   6 pair per sq km on Doune CBC (85 % of 1996). 1 at Dunblane 27 Aug bathed in rain runoff from eaves (NB).

ROBIN *Erithacus rubecula (B,W)*
Under-recorded (Ed). BBS shows 21 per 10 km in conifers, 8 on farmland & 15 in 'Urban'.
C   2 AoT on 5 km of lower Devon (2 in 1996) (CJH).
S   4 pairs per sq Km on Doune CBC, much as 1996, 1st juv seen 4 Jun (NB). Autumn song at Airthrey from 6 Aug, sang at night on 18 Jan (CJH AT).

REDSTART *Phoenicurus phoenicurus (B)*
1st records 1 (F) L.Katrine on 30 Apr, 4 Balquhidder 3 May (DAC BDA). In Aug 2 juv in heather at Invertrossachs on 3rd & a M Alva on 25th would have left breeding territories (DAC PMA).
S   44 nest attempts at Trossachs colony produced 240 Y, number of pairs up 50 % (HR). F with Juv Buchlyvie 10 Aug was 1st record in 4 years (suggests local breeding, Ed) (DAC).

WHINCHAT *Saxicola rubetra (B)*
BBS shows 5 per 10 km in conifers, 4 on moorland & 1 on farmland. 1st records: 2 BoA 20 Apr; 1 Balquhidder on 3 May & 2 Glen Buckie on 5th (AT BDA DT). Autumn migrants: 2 Kinneil 30 Aug, 1 Higgins Neuk on 6 Sep & 2 Skinflats on 13th (DMB DSF DAC).
S   8 pairs Braes of Doune (Drumloist) 12 May (DOE), c10 Inverlochlarig 18 Jul (DT), widespread Braeleny-A'Chroin 30 May. However scarce on heather Ben Bhreac (L.Ard Forest) 23 May (CJH).

*STONECHAT *Saxicola torquata (b,w)*
Breeding population seems very small (Ed).
F   1 L.Ellrig 23 Nov (BDA).
S   M Doune Ponds 5 Apr & M Flanders Moss on 19th (AD SS). Pair Glen Finglas 5 Oct & M on 25 Nov. 2 Cocksburn on 29 Oct. Pair Braeleny 11 Nov (DMB AT DJC).

WHEATEAR *Oenanthe oenanthe (B)*
BBS shows 7 per 10 km on moorland & 3 in moor/conifer edge.
M Barbush 16 Mar – very early (WRB). Most 1st records in April: 1 Braeval on 6th, Earlsburn Res on 5th, 14 Kinneil on 6th, Inverlochlarig & Glen Finglas on 12th; on estuary to 9 May with 4 Bandeath on 4th & 3 Skinflats on 5th. (DT MT DAC SS DMB GO). Autumn migrants at Kinneil & Skinflats included 6 on 30 Sep & 1 on 5 Oct (DSF DT).
S   20 pairs Inverlochlarig 2 Aug (DOE). 2 AoT Braeleny 30 May, 2 pairs + juvs Glen Lochay 16 Jul (CJH WRB).

*RING OUSEL   Turdus torquatus (b)
S   1 Monachyle Glen 21 Apr & 1 Cruach Ardrain on 25th (AD DOE). 5 Rhuveag 5 May (DT). 2 M Ben Each 15 Jun & anxious pair Glen Ogle (DMB DOE).

BLACKBIRD   Turdus merula (B,W)
     BBS shows 113 per 10 km in 'Urban', 16 on farmland & 10 in conifers.
C   8 AoT on 5 km of lower Devon, 9 in 1996 (CJH).
S   13 pairs per sq km on Doune CBC, 72 % of 1996, 1st juv seen 6 May (NB).

FIELDFARE   Turdus pilaris (W)
     Spring departure ceased early and included 55 Plean CP & 200 Thornhill 29 Mar & 125 Trossachs on 30th, 110 Cocksburn 6 Apr & 40 Stronend on 8th (DT JS HR AT DAC).
     1st of autumn 5 Kinneil 5 Oct, then 200 ->SW Lecropt on 17th, 12 Gargunnock on 18th & 320 Cambus on 19th. Large parties widespread to mid Nov, max 700 Thornhill Carse 23 Oct, 3000 Flanders Moss 2 Nov & 500 Slamannan 15 Nov. Visible movement included flights to east: 40 Dunipace 23 Oct & 260 Callander 4 Nov. In Dec only 120 Alva on 24th (AB DT DAC CJH DOE MVB WRB NB PMA).
F   18 on shore Bo'ness 2 Jan (AS). 210 Skinflats 1 Jan (MVB).
S   220 Kippen 9 Feb (DAC).

SONG THRUSH   Turdus philomelos (B,W)
     BBS shows 12 per 10 km in conifers, 7 farmland, & 6 'Urban'. Few in mid-winter – 1 BoA 28 Nov (AT).
F   Numerous, with Blackbirds, Skinflats 28 Sep – presumed migrants (AB).
C   2 AoT in 5 Km lower Devon, 1 in 1995 (CJH).
     Regular in Stirling garden from 16 Feb, juvs seen 8 Jun but one struck a window and another predated (RJ). By contrast, 1 in Grangemouth garden 3 Jul was "a very rare bird !" (GO).

REDWING   Turdus iliacus (W)
     1st of autumn 2 Doune 25 Sep & 3->SW Airthrey on 30th, then none till 20 Tullibody Inch 13 Oct & 16 Skinflats on 14th.Large parties widespread from 19 Oct, max 400 Flanders Moss 2 Nov & 200 Slamannan on 15th. Visible movement: 100->SW Lecropt 17 Oct; on 4 Nov 100->E Callander & 95 ->E Cromlix. Much scarcer through December – 102 Cambus on 27th (DOE DMB CJH GO WRB BRT).
S   Flocks of 20 to 50 in Jan & Feb (DJC MVB), none March.

MISTLE THRUSH   Turdus viscivorus (B,W)
     Under-recorded. BBS shows 3 per 10 km in conifers but none in 'Urban'.
S   1 AoT Plean CP 19 Apr (AB). 33 L.Dhu (Rusky) 7 Aug (AT), 60 Braes of Doune 4 Oct (DOE). Scarce in winter – 1 Menstrie 2 Jan & 1 Balquhidder 28 Nov (BRT DJC).

GRASSHOPPER WARBLER *Locustella naevia (b)*
> More this year.
F   1 Skinflats 30 Apr to 15 Jul. 1 Kinneil 14 Jun to 10 Aug (AB BDA GO DT).
C   3 singing Devon WBS 30 Apr then none to 17 Jun (CJH). Song at Cambus Pools 9 Aug (WRB).
S   1Aberfoyle 2 May (DAC). 3 Flanders Moss 15 May (TJ). 2 Inverlochlarig 18 Jul & 1 at two other sites Balquhidder 19 & 26 Jul (DT WRB). 3 Drip carse 14 Jul & 1 Gartmore on 21st (WRB).

SEDGE WARBLER *Acrocephalus schoenobaenus (B)*
F   1 Kinneil on 3 May & 3 on 4th; last 1 on 7 Sep (GO DT).
C   2 AoT Cambus, last on 24 Aug (CJH WRB). 54 AoT on Devon WBS, none on 30 Apr but 70% arrived by 10 May, still 2 arriving 11 Jun; last 6 on 13 Aug (CJH).
    3 Aberfoyle & M Ashfield 10 May (DAC WRB).1 AoT Doune CBC from 19 May (NB). Bred L.Dhu (Rusky) (AT).

LESSER WHITETHROAT *Sylvia curruca*
F   1 Skinflats, with Willow Warblers, 3 Aug (DT).

WHITETHROAT *Sylvia communis (B)*
> BBS shows 6 per 10 km in 'Urban', 2 on farmland & 1 in conifers.
> 1st record a very early bird Brig o'Turk 13 Apr (DOE), most in May: Bandeath & Plean on 4th, Doune on 5th (DMB DT NB).
F   Bred Skinflats, last 2 on 20 Sep (AB DT). 1 Kinneil 20 Sep (DAC)
C   9 AoT on Devon WBS (as 1996), none on 30 Apr but 6 by 10 May; last 5 on 13 Aug (CJH).
SWP   5 pairs per sq km Doune CBC, as 1996; 1st juv on 23 Jun (NB).

GARDEN WARBLER *Sylvia borin (B)*
> 1st records in May: Bridge of Allan & Lake of Menteith on 7th, R.Devon (all AoT) on 10th, Braes of Doune on 12th (AT DOE CJH).
C   5 AoT Devon WBS (CJH).

BLACKCAP *Sylvia atricapilla (B)*
> Under-recorded as breeder (Ed)
> Winter records: F Alva 1 Jan, F Falkirk 21 Dec (PMA JW).
F   F Grangemouth 25 Sep (GO), 1 Skinflats 17 & 28 Sep (AB). M Bo'ness 3 Nov (AS).
C   1st Cambus 20 Apr (DMB). M Alva 4 & 21 Oct (PMA).
S   M Blairlogie 15 Apr (DAC). 1 AoT Doune CBC from 7 May (NB).

WOOD WARBLER *Phylloscopus sibilatrix (B)*
> 1 L.Katrine 30 Apr, other 1st records in May: 2 Balquhidder on 5th, BoA (3) on 7th, L.Ard(Doon Hill, 6) on 9th, L.Ard Forest (Couligart) on 12th, 1 Howierigg on 14th (DAC DT AT DOE MA).

CHIFFCHAFF *Phylloscopus collybita (B)*
> 1st records in March: Alva 15th, BoA 17th, Blairlogie 20th, Lake of Menteith 22nd, Carriden 23rd, Grangemouth 25th, Stirling 27th,

Larbert & Plean CP 29th (PMA AT MA DAC AS GO DT). Last, 1 Grangemouth 25 Sep & 2 Ashfield on 29th, 1 Plean CP 19 Oct (GO WRB AB).

WILLOW WARBLER *Phylloscopus trochilus (B)*
1st records in April: 1 Doune Ponds & Lake of Menteith on 8th, Skinflats & Buchlyvie on 11th, Ashfield (3), Menteith Hills (6) and Devon WBS (4) on 12th, Stirling & Kinneil & Gartmorn Dam(10) on 14th (DOE GO DAC WRB DT CJH RJ PMA). Autumn dispersal noted with juvs in Stirling garden from 6 Jul, 15 Skinflats on 3 Aug & 16 Cambus Pools on 8th, 100 Killin 15 Sep. Last Buchlyvie & Stirling 21 Sep(RJ DT DSF PWS DAC).
BBS shows 107 per 10 km in conifers, 21 in farmland (NB).
C 14 AoT on 5 km of lower Devon, 12 in 1996 (CJH).
S 9 pairs per sq km on Doune CBC, as 1996 (NB).

GOLDCREST *Regulus regulus (B,W)*
Greatly under-recorded (Ed). BBS shows 44 per 10 km in conifers, 3 on farmland (NB).
F Through year at Skinflats (AB).1 Kinneil 16 Sep & 31 Dec (GO BDA).
S Regular in Stirling garden Sep, Nov, Dec (RJ).

SPOTTED FLYCATCHER *Muscicapa striata (B)*
Under-recorded (Ed). Scarce in BBS, 0.7 per 10 km, only in farmland (NB).
1st records: in May, Gartmore 11th, Ashfield 12th, Alva 28th & Buchlyvie 30th ; (DAC WRB PMA). Last, 1 Skinflats 6 Sep (BDA).
S In summer also at Killin, L.Ard Forest, Aberfoyle, Balquhidder (Inverlochlarig & Rhuveag), Plean CP (PWS CJH DAC JMi DT WRB AB).

PIED FLYCATCHER *Ficedula hypoleuca (b)*
1st records: L.Ard Forest 27 Apr, Balquhidder (Rhuveag 5) on 3 May, L.Katrine on 10th (DOE BDA DAC).
S 62 nest attempts at Trossachs colony, 320 Y reared, another 6 nests produced 29 Y (HR). F Killin 18 May (PWS).

LONG-TAILED TIT *Aegithalos caudatus (B,W)*
F 28 Bo'ness 17 Nov & 26 on 21st (AS). 4 Kinneil 4 Nov & 7 on 21 Dec (GO BDA).
C 15 Cambus Pools 20 Dec (WRB).
S 17 Loch Ard Forest 26 Aug; 12 L.Venachar 23 Nov (CJH). 13 Callander 7 Oct; 17 Brig o'Turk 25 Nov (DJC). Max 8 Stirling 6 Oct (RJ), 13 Riverside 10 Nov & 16 Forthbank 15 Dec (AT).1 AoT on Doune CBC (NB).

COAL TIT *Parus ater (B,W)*
Greatly under-recorded (Ed). BBS shows 44 records per 10 km in conifers, 3 on farmland (NB).
F In Nov/Dec almost as common as Blue Tits in Polmont (JW) – but in

Grangemouth 3 in garden 29 Sep was "big count" (GO).
S   At Glenartney col on 19 Sep, 6 with Blue Tits in a small plantation flew off W toward Callendar (CJH).

BLUE TIT *Parus caeruleus (B,W)*
Under-recorded (Ed). BBS shows 35 per 10 km in 'urban' squares, 26 on farmland & 17 in conifers.
C   9 Menstrie 2 Jan (BRT). 10 in Alva garden Jan to Feb (PMA). 7 AoT on 5 Km of lower Devon, 4 in 1996 (CJH).
S   50 Dunblane 17 Jul (MVB). 7 pair per sq km on Doune CBC, 12 in 1996 (NB). Breeding population in Trossachs up 200 % on 1996 (HR).

GREAT TIT *Parus major (B,W)*
Under-recorded (Ed). BBS shows 18 per 10 km in conifers, 14 on farmland and 8 in 'Urban' squares.
C   5 AoT on 5 km of lower Devon, 2 in 1996(CJH).
S   Singing in mild weather 13 Jan & 28 Nov (AT). 7 AoT per sq km on Doune CBC, 8.5 in 1996 (NB). Breeding population in Trossachs up 150 % on 1996 (HR).

TREECREEPER *Certhia familiaris (B,W)*
Under-recorded (Ed). BBS shows 1 per 10 km on farmland.
Recorded from Bo'ness, Skinflats, Callander, Leny (AS GO DJC). Pair nested in willow by Carron at Camelon, 5Y fledged 23 May (MA).

JAY *Garrulus glandarius (B,W)*
BBS records largely from conifers, 2 per 10km.
F   All year at Torwood (AB) – continuous with range around Stirling (Ed).
C   Recorded Alva in Jun & Dec, Gartmorn/Fishcross in Jan-Feb (PMA).
S   Recorded from some 24 sites from Killin & L.Ard Forest to Blairlogie & North Third; no records from north edge of Gargunnocks. Max 12 Strathyre 16 Sep (AT).

MAGPIE *Pica pica (B,W)*
Its abundance around Stirling is not necessarily noted in the west and east of the area (Ed). BBS shows 33 per 10 km in 'urban' squares, 5 in farmland & 1 in conifers.
F   5 Skinflats 21 Feb & 30 Mar (GO AB). 8 Larbert 12 Dec (NB).
C   3 AoT on 5 km of lower Devon, 4 in 1996 (CJH).
S   20 Lecropt 9 Nov, 20 BoA 10 Sep, 13 Forthbank 14 Dec (DT CJH AT), but roost numbers higher: 44 Airthrey 27 Feb & 35 on 10 Dec (MVB). 1 AoT on Doune CBC (NB). 2 Sheriffmuir 18 Sep, in conifers at 230m. 1 Blairdrummond 26 Sep & 1 nearby on 14 May were both first records for NB & CJH. At W end of range, 3 Kippen 11 Apr &1 Lake of Menteith 19 Mar (NB).

JACKDAW *Corvus monedula (B,W)*
An overlooked species, about 5 reports (Ed). BBS shows highest frequency in urban areas.

S   400 Killin 21 Jan (PWS). Max 200 on roost flight Callander 29 Oct (DJC). 100 BoA 28 Nov (AT). 4 pair per sq km on Doune CBC, as 1996; 1st juvs 23 Jun (NB).

ROOK   Corvus frugilegus (B,W)
Rookery counts: BoA(N) 25 in decid, 122 in pines; BoA(S) 161; Witches Craig 55; Myretoun 65; 58 Menstrie nursery (new in 1996). Total 486 (522 in 1996) (CJH). Survey of 72 rookeries in Stirling district counted 2134 nests; largest 173 Buchlyvie & 171 Craigforth (NB).

CARRION CROW   Corvus corone (B,W)
Possibly the most widespread species: BBS shows 59 per 10 km in 'Urban' squares, 38 in farmland & 37 on moorland.
F   143 Kinneil 3 May, feeding on musselbank (GO).
C   40 Cambus Pools 19 Jul (CJH).
S   6 AoT per km sq at Doune CBC (NB). Birds with white wingstripes seen Riverside 10 Nov & 16 Dec (AT). Hoodies: 9 records (including hybrids) were from the usual breeding range N & W of Lake of Menteith (DAC DJC), plus 1 Kippen 18 Jan & 1 L.Mahaick 2 Nov (NB DOE).

RAVEN   Corvus corax (B,W)
S   15 territories checked, 11 pairs, 8 successful pairs of which 3 raised 11Y (PSA). 18 Glen Artney col 11 Nov & 14 Meall na Iolaire 12 Dec (DJC). Outwith of immediate breeding areas: 1 L.Ard Forest 25 Aug, 1 Lake of Menteith 25 Oct (DT CJH). 2 Earls Hill 2 Aug (CJM).

STARLING   Sturnus vulgaris (B,W)
Greatly underreported (Ed). BBS show most frequent in 'Urban' squares.
F   Post breeding arrival at Kinneil, 150 on 14 Jun (DT). 1220 Kincardine Bridge roost 26 Oct & 1550 on 7 Nov (CJH).
C   Roosts: Cambus Haugh reedbed 5700 on 28 Aug; Tullibody Inch 2700 on 27 Sep & 13 Oct (CJH).
S   11 AoT per sq km on Doune CBC, 16 in 1996; fledglings from 4 Jun (NB).

HOUSE SPARROW   Passer domesticus (B,W)
Under-recorded (Ed). BBS shows mainly in 'Urban' areas.
F   60 Higgins Neuk 25 Sep (DSF). 30 Dunipace 6 Nov (CJH).
S   14 pairs per sq km on Doune CBC as 1996; fledglings from 21 May (NB). 35 Ashfield 2 Aug (WRB). 30 Killin 9 Aug (PWS).

TREE SPARROW   Passer montanus (B,W)
F   5 by R.Carron at Larbert 29 Mar (GO JMr). 4 Maddiston 14 to 30 Dec (JW). 1 Grangemouth 6 Oct – "great tick on feeder" (GO).
C   3 Cambus 19 Sep (WRB).
S   Lecropt: max 60 on 2 Jan to 13 on 15 Mar; 15 on 9 Nov, max 40 on 13 Dec (WRB DT AD DAC CJM). 20 Blairdrummond Carse 20 Dec. 1 Arnprior 21 Sep (DAC). 15 Cambuskenneth 10 Mar (AT).

CHAFFINCH *Fringilla coelebs (B,W)*
> BBS shows 75 per 10 km in conifers, 51 on farmland & 25 in 'Urban' squares.

F   230 Drumbowie 11 Nov (NB); 50 Skinflats 27 Dec (AB).

C   13 AoT on lower Devon in May, 16 in 1996 (CJH).

S   28 pairs per sq km on Doune CBC, 34 in 1996 (NB). 250 Kippen & 300 Thornhill 2 Nov; 300 Doune 29 Nov (DOE). 600 Argaty 221 Dec (WRB). 2000 Kinbuck 23 Nov (MVB).

BRAMBLING *Fringilla montifringilla (W)*

F   12 Avonbridge 4 Mar (MA).

S   600 Kinbuck on 3 Jan, only 5 on 23 Nov (MVB). 15 L.Lubnaig 11 Jan & 90 (under Oak-Beech) L.Voil on 28th (RB NB). 18 L.Venachar 9 Feb & 29 Glen Tye on 13th (WRB DSF). Scarce in autumn: earliest 1 Glen Finglas 9 Oct (DMB), 5 Kinbuck 23 Nov (MVB).

GREENFINCH *Carduelis chloris (B,W)*
> Underrecorded. BBS shows 39 per 10 km in 'Urban' squares, 3 in farmland & in conifers.

F   35 Skinflats 5 Aug & 50 from 16th to 31st; 50 on 27 Dec (DT AB). Max 8 at feeder Bo'ness Jan-May & Dec (AS).
     160 Cambuskenneth 10 Jan (CJH). 150 Kinbuck 28 Sep (MVB). 40 L.Watston 12 Dec & 50 Thornhill (rape stubble) on 16th (CJH NB).

GOLDFINCH *Carduelis carduelis (B,W)*
> BBS shows 6 per 10 km in farmland and 5 in 'Urban" squares.

F   18 Kinneil 2 Jan & 25 on 5 Oct (DT). 12 Skinflats 22 Feb, 15 on 22 Apr & 18 on 17 Sep (DAC GO). 120 on saltmarsh Kincardine Bridge 14 Dec (MVB). 18 Larbert 4 Jan; 30 Camelon 1 Oct (MA). 16 Polmont 21 Dec (resident flock JW).

C   4 AoT on Devon WBS, 3 in 1996. 20 Menstrie 8 Jan & 21 on Burdock on 29 Dec (PMA BRT).

S   2 pairs per sq km on Doune CBC, 2 in 1996 (NB). 130 Kinbuck 12 Jan (MVB). 10 Killin 17 Mar (PWS).16 Braes of Doune 29 Jan & 40 on 4 Oct. 15 L.Venachar 8 Oct & 23 Keltie Glen on 20th (DOE DJC). 120 Thornhill in uncut Rape 8 Oct (NB).

SISKIN *Carduelis spinus (B,W)*
> BBS shows 34 per 10 km in conifers, 2 on farmland.

F   28 Wallacebank Wood 20 Aug (AS). 15 Grangemouth 26 Sep was garden record (GO). 100 on Knapweed at Union Canal 20 & 21 Sep (JW).

C   30 Alva 7 Aug to 30 Sep (PMA). Many parties Gartmorn 11 Sep (CJH).

S   lst of winter at Stirling feeder on 22 Jan, a few to end Feb (RJ). 120 Balquhidder (Kirkton) 1 Jan, 30 L.Lubnaig on 11th (WRB RB). 60 Doune 16 Feb (DOE). Abundant Carron Valley Res 13 Apr, 30 on 10 Sep. 30 Port of Menteith 2 Jul, 20 Glen Lochay on 16th & 24 Inverlochlarig on 18th (CJH WRB DT). 200 Kippen 1 Aug (AT). 55 in Beech at BoA 8 Aug & 130 Airthrey on 11th (CJH MVB). 200 in Rape stubble at Thornhill 10 Sep (M Evans).

LINNET   *Carduelis cannabina (B,W)*

    BBS shows 5 per 10 km on moorland, 4 in conifers, 3 on farmland & 2 in 'Urban'.

F   100 Skinflats 31 Aug & 60 on 27 Dec (DT AB). 20 Higgins Neuk 6 Sep (DSF). 18 on shore Bo'ness 31 Dec (AS).

C   70 Menstrie 2 Jan (BRT).

    3 AoT on Doune CBC, 1 in 1996 (NB).10 AoT Braes Doune (Drumloist) 12 May (DOE). 650 on uncut Rape at Thornhill 8 Oct & 300 on the stubble 17 Dec (NB). 1200 Thornhill Carse 9 Nov (MVB).120 Lanrick & 200 Kinbuck 28 Sep, 100 in stubble L.Watston 12 Dec (DOE MVB CJH)

TWITE   *Carduelis flavirostris (b,W)*

    BBS shows 1 per 10 km on moorland.

F   10 Kinneil 2 Jan & 1 on 13 Oct (DT AB). 100 Kincardine Bridge 14 Dec (MVB).

C   1 with Linnets Menstrie 2 Jan (BRT).

    Spring/summer reports from Inverlochlarig (20), Glen Buckie, Aberfoyle, Braeleny, Stuc a'Chroin (CJH DT DOE SS). 120 Kippenrait 6 Jan (RB). 400 Kinbuck on 3 Jan to 41 on 23 Mar, 300 on 1 Nov (MVB NB). 25 Glenartney col 19 Sep & 1 Stronend on 25th (CJH DOE).

REDPOLL   *Carduelis flammea (B,W)*

    BBS shows 17 per 10 km in conifers.

F   3 in Bo'ness garden 31 Jan (AS). 4 Union Canal 20 Sep (JW). 5 Kinneil 6 Nov (GO), of 15 on 14 Dec 10 were typical *C.f.cabaret* but 5 showed features of *C.f.flammea* with paler plumage (especially below), streaked whitish rumps & bulkier with deeper calls (DMB).

C   10 on Tansy at Cambus 27 Dec (BRT).

S   Several displaying groups Carron Valley Res 13 Apr (CJH). 35 Inverlochlarig 18 Jul (DT). 16 Dunblane 22 Jan (AT).

COMMON CROSSBILL   *Loxia curvirostra (b,W)*

    BBS shows 14 per 10 km in conifers

S   15 Flanders Moss, near Ward Toll, 3 Jan (DT). Widespread L.Ard Forest 9 Feb, 2 families 9 Apr, 15 on 18 Jul & 5 on 21st 5 km to S (CJH DOE WRB). 6 Aberfoyle 14 Feb & 2 families on 6 Apr (DOE). Song at Carron Valley Forest in early spring,13 on 21 Oct (DJB GO). 35 L.Rusky 9 Nov. 3 North Third 15 May. 11BoA 6 Jun to 5 on 12 Jul. 12 Braes of Doune 28 Sep & 23 Oct. 8 Dunblane 21 Oct & 5 on 13 Nov (MVB BDA CJH DMB DOE).

COMMON ROSEFINCH   *Carpodacus erythrinus*

S   An adult male singing at Inverlochlarig (Balquhidder) 22 Jun to 14 Jul. The bird was found and identified by D Greenwood and reported to Birdline Scotland, who have supplied the dates. It was seen by many observers but the only description is from GO (5 Jul) who noted the scarlet red head nape, throat, breast and rump; upperparts dull oatmeal brown with prominent rusty-brown double wing bar, heavy & slate coloured bill, dark eye, pale straw legs. This is the first record for the area. The species is a late migrant and seems to be slowly colonising the UK after a prolonged westward spread through northern Europe. At this stage in an expansion of range it is typical for males to appear and sing but fail to find mates.

BULLFINCH *Pyrrhula pyrrhula (B,W)*
BBS shows 4 per 10 km in conifers & 2 on farmland.
Widespread in groups less than ten.
C   10 Upper Glendevon* 29 Jan (MA).
       In spring at Stirling fed on buds of Greengage, Amelanchier, Apple (RJ). 9 Glen Tye* 13 Feb (DSF). 11 Doune 16 Sep, 12 L.Ard Forest 15 Oct (DOE DJC). *exposed high ground in midwinter.*

*SNOW BUNTING *Plectrophenax nivalis (W)*
C   F/Imm Bengengie 29 Jan (MA).
S   5 Craigmore (Aberfoyle) 14 Feb (DOE). 2 Glen Lochay 23 Nov & 1 Glen Buckie on 30th (DMB DT).

YELLOWHAMMER *Emberiza citrinella (B,W)*
BBS shows 6 per 10 km on farmland & 5 in conifers.
C   9 AoT in 5 km on lower Devon, 14 in 1996 (CJH). 30 Gartmorn 16 Dec (PMA).
S   10 AoT per sq km on Doune CBC, 20 in 1996 (NB). 2 singing Glen Lochay (Low Botaurie) 15 Jul (WRB) *scarce in smaller highland glens, Ed.* Thornhill Carse: 40 on 5 Jan, 9 Feb & 2 Nov. 40 Blairdrummond Carse 20 Dec (DAC DOE)

REED BUNTING *Emberiza schoeniclus (B,W)*
BBS shows 2 per 10 km in farmland and 'Urban' & 1 in conifers and moorland.
C   10 AoT on Devon WBS, 13 in 1996 (CJH). 7 Cambus Pools 20 Dec (WRB) & 7 Alva Ponds on 24th (BRT). 10 Menstrie 2 Jan & 12 on 29 Dec (BRT).
S   1 AoT on Doune CBC (NB). Widespread Braeleny-A'Chroin 30 May (CJH). 10 Thornhill Carse & 10 Lecropt on 2 Nov (DOE DT).

CORN BUNTING *Emberiza calandra*
No records.

ESCAPED SPECIES

BLACK SWAN *Cygnus atratus*
C   2 Gartmorn 27 Oct to 7 Dec (PMA DAC AT)

WOOD DUCK *Aix sponsa*
F   F on R.Carron , Larbert, 11 Mar (MA). *(Only an excellent view that gave a detailed description and sketch allowed separation from F Mandarin, Ed.)*

RED-LEGGED PARTRIDGE *Alectoris rufa*
S   Apparently regularly released Cromlix: 2M countercalling 4 Nov, 29 on 23rd (CJH MVB). Also noted above BoA Apr & Oct (AD AT).

BOOK REVIEWS/NOTES (Naturalist)

Discovering the Firth of Forth. W. F. Hendrie. Edinburgh, 1998. 285pp. ISBN 0-85976-458-3. £9.95.

This book provides a wealth of detail on the history of the coastline of the Firth of Forth, from North Queensferry to Fife Ness on the northern (Fife) coast, and from Dalmeny to Coldingham on the southern (Lothian) shore. In an easy to read style the author takes the reader for a walk along the shorelines of the Firth describing the town and villages along the way, with a wealth of detail on their history. There is a particular emphasis on the history and development of the settlements in the last 100 years, with a wealth of detail on the ups and down of the shipping trade and of the vessels which ply on the Forth. All the recent history is also set in the context of the history of Scotland back to the 12th century.

It is clear that the Firth of Forth has played a vital role throughout Scottish history. In earlier centuries the Forth provided Scotland's main trading route, and although the Clyde eclipsed that role for many years, the Forth is again now the main trading connection for Scotland. This book shows that the shores of the Firth of Forth are fascinating places to explore, and I am sure that this book will encourage many to discover it for themselves.

D.S. McLusky

The Glasgow Naturalist

The May issue of the *Glasgow Naturalist* (vol. 23, 3) includes these items of interest. Wildlife conservation in Glasgow Parks; Loch Lomondside depicted and described, myths, marvels and monsters; The Haloscene history of Scots Pine at Loch Sloy; Whale lice from stranded whales in the Firth of Forth; Scottish insect records for 1996, a 15p supplement on the Natural History of Glasgow's Botanic Gardens; Legacy of the Loch Lomond Wolf; Old limestone workings, further notes; spread of the Orange Tip butterly in Scotland; mink in the Forth and Clyde Canal; 8pp of book reviews.

L.C.

BO'MAINS MEADOW – BO'NESS

Angus Smith

Bo'mains Meadow, a small herb rich hay meadow, is situated on the north facing slope near to the top of the Airngath Hill, on the urban fringe of Bo'ness, about three-quarters-of-a-mile west of the A706 road between Linlithgow and Bo'ness (Grid Ref: NS 988 794 – OS Sheet 65). The meadow is part of a Scottish Wildlife Trust (SWT) Reserve and access to it is from an unclassified road and a gate at its south-west corner, where there is room to park a single vehicle on the grass verge (Figure 1).

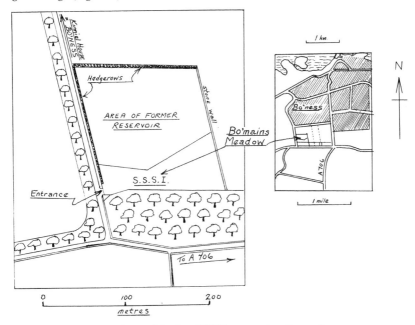

Figure 1 Bo'mains Meadow SWT Reserve – location and access.

The meadow is a remnant (0.94 ha – 2.32 acres) of species rich neutral grassland and it is known to have been virtually untouched, apart from light grazing, since 1884 (Salmon, 1913) when it was acquired by the former West Lothian County Council as part of the lands of Borrowstoun Service Reservoir.

On Local Authority Regionalisation in 1975 ressponsibility for the reservoir was transferred to Central Regional Council and the Bo'ness area became part of the secondary Falkirk District Council area. In 1990 Bo'mains Service Reservoir, immediately adjoining the meadow on its north side, was drained, the earth walls bulldozed inwards and the area seeded with grass. The meadow, however, was left intact and continued to flourish.

Late in 1990 local rumour began to circulate to the effect that the area of the former reservoir was to be used for a housing development and because of the perceived threat to the meadow the author approached the SWT suggesting that they endeavour to acquire the meadow and area of the former reservoir as a wildlife reserve. The Nature Conservancy Council (now Scottish Natural Heritage) designated the Meadow a Site of Special Scientific Interest (SSSI) on 5th February 1991, and the SWT then came to an informal management agreement with Central Regional Council to manage the meadow until it was finally decided whether or not the land would be disposed.

In 1996 the unitary Local Authorities and Water Board areas were established and Bo'ness came under the jurisdication of the new Falkirk Council. Ownership of the former reservoir lands then passed to the East of Scotland Water Board and negotiations between the Water Board and SWT were pursued until finally, in June 1998, agreement was reached and Bo'mains Meadow, together with the area of the former reservoir (1.736 ha – 3.79 acres) became an SWT Reserve and has SWT ownership.

The meadow is considered to be of national importance and is sheltered on its west and south sides by belts of trees. To date seventy-six vascular plant species have been recorded including Common Twayblade (*Listera ovata*), Common spotted-orchid (*Dactylorhiza fuchsii*), Northern Marsh-orchid (*Dactylorhiza purpurella*), and Greater Butterfly-orchid (*Platanthera chlorantha*). In addition there is a good variety of hay meadow grasses and other plants such as Lady's-mantle (*Alchemilla xanthochlora*), Mouse-ear-hawkweed (*Pilosella officinarum*), Common Knapweed (*Centaurea nigra*), Meadow Vetchling (*Lathyrus pratensis*), Yellow-rattle (*Rhinanthus minor*), Tufted Vetch (*Vicia cracca*) and Water Avens (*Geum rivale*).

Management of the Reserve follows the regime adopted over the past century. This entails cutting hay in late August and clearing it from the site. Initially the hay was spread on the former reservoir to benefit that area from residual seed and this appears to have been successful, as a good variety of plants from the meadow are now appearing there. A specialist company has been employed during the last three harvests, and it gathers the seed for a seed bank and subsequent distribution to create new meadows elsewhere.

Foxes (*Vulpes vulpes*) have been observed passing through the Reserve and Grey Partridges (*Perdix perdix*) are known to have successfully nested. The meadow also has a large variety of invertebrate species, which have still to be properly surveyed, and is habitat for a variety of smaller mammals and birds.

There is little doubt that Bo'mains Meadow is a remnant of what the surrounding uncultivated agricultural land would have been like in 1884 and has many species which have been lost elsewhere. Visitors are welcome, but are asked to exercise due care regarding the sensitivity of the site and the rarity of a number of the species it contains by refraining from picking flowers or digging up plants.

Reference

Salmon, T. J. (1913). *Borrowstounness and District*. William Hodge & Company: Edinburgh & London.

DAVID DOUGLAS OF THE FIRS

Archie Smith

Great trees grow up the Teith and upper Forth valleys. Spires in a sylvan landscape, they leave behind the matrix of native species and earlier European introduced specimens. West of Stirling they thrive on the increasingly wetter climate similar to home, the wet west Pacific coast of North America.

Keir, Blairdrummond, Doune Lodge, Lendrick, all have still the arboretums commenced over a century and a half ago. Cambusmore entrance commences an area of fine specimens in and around Callander. Over the hill, the Forth valley too has many of those sylvan spires, especially at Cardross and Gartmore.

All stand as monuments to a trio of Taysiders who became, after further education at the Edinburgh and Glasgow Botanic Gardens, scientific travellers. Archibald Menzies, David Douglas, and John Jeffries over the period 1792 to 1851, were involved in exploration, scientific survey, and plant procurement. Their main focus was on that part of North America west of the Pacific Mountain chain. Current American writers call it "Ecotopia", ecological utopia. John Muir of Dunbar, the father of the American conservation movement, declared that all America was a garden before European settlement and exploitation.

The trio of travellers all made a contribution to enriching the gardens of Europe, but the greatest of all was David Douglas. His contribution amounted to over 200 plants; flowers, shrubs, and tall trees. A recent traveller visiting a substantial section of the preserved remnant of the Pacific Temperate Rain Forest declared, "Douglas Fir is king".

So it is in the arboreta of the Forth and Teith. Two specimens on Scottish sites tie for the record of the tallest tree overall in the British Isles. They stand at 212 feet, and many of our trees in those valleys will catch up in the not too distant future.

An impressive monument to David Douglas stands beside the old Parish Church at the village of New Scone, erected in 1840. Near the town cross of the medieval burgh of Scone, a lone marker of the site, stands the oldest Douglas Fir growing in the British Isles. A notice tells that it was grown from seed sent from the Columbia River of north west America in 1826, by David Douglas. His first employer, the third Earl of Mansefield, was first to receive this bounty. The tree stands today, an arboreal monument to an adventurer.

When, in April 1825, David Douglas arrived at the mouth of the Columbia River only five fur trade forts followed its course as available bases; south of similar Russian settlements in Alaska and north of Spanish California. Most of the time he was alone with the native Americans. He was helped and hindered by the Indians. Unable to understand a white man who was not greedy for pelts and sought plants, they thought him mad. He was called 'The Grass Man', one to be exploited or at least humoured. They soon came to respect him as 'one of King George's Chiefs'. His journals tell tales of treachery and extraordinary kindness. He lived in their lodges and recorded their lives for posterity.

Once a year, a little party left the Columbia River base, Fort Vancouver, and paddling and portaging, crossed the Rocky Mountains and away on to Hudson Bay. Most years their journey was an epic of adventure. Not satisfied with one year's gleaning in the wilderness, David Douglas had decided to stay a second one. He might have then returned then as he came, by sea. However, to cross the great continent was too much of a challenge to pass over. He came home by Hudson Bay during 1827.

Initially lionised in London by the scientific society of his day he soon found fame to be fickle. He longed to return to go further north. In time opportunity came. With a remit to survey the great river as a possible boundary between the United States and the United Kingdom's territories west of the Rockies, he returned to the Columbia. This time being a plant procurer was a cover. He had multiple sponsors, but he had also his own agenda.

With the help of the Russian Government, David Douglas intended to travel by Alaska through Siberia to Europe. He set out on this secret mission and reached northern New Caledonia as British Columbia was then designated. It was more than his broken body could achieve. Broken, blind in one eye, beaten in spirit, he turned back. This time he intended to return home by Hawaii. Still the explorer, he met his end there in a tragic accident in 1834, aged 35.

Next year is the bi-centenary of his birth. A David Douglas Society has been formed to ensure it does not pass unobserved in Scotland. A long established one in North America will complement the celebration on that continent. At appropriate places they intend to erect monuments.

Further Reading

All for a Handful of Seed: the Life and Adventures of David Douglas. A. K. Smith, 16 Katrine Crescent, Callander, FK17 8JS. 95pp, 1997. ISBN 1-900489-08-2, £7.99.

For information on the David Douglas Society contact the author.

LAWHILL COMMUNITY WOODLAND – A YEAR ON

Martin Boardman
Eamonn Wall & Co.

It is now two years since local landowner and Lord Lieutenant of Clackmannanshire, Col. Robert Stewart, identified the need for an accessible place close to Dollar where locals could come and enjoy the countryside.

After consultation, a 24 acre agricultural site was duly identified by Col. Stewart, and with the assistance of Dollar based woodland design and management company Eamonn Wall & Co., a mixture of broadleaved and coniferous trees were planted to create a varied and attractive woodland.

The site, situated to the north east of Dollar, lies in the valley of the Kelly burn and extends up the lower north facing slopes of Lawhill. The highest points afford good views over the rest of the site and across the valley to the Ochils. Much of Dollar and its surrounding area is visible and the high rise flats of Glasgow can be seen on a clear day. The top of Lawhill is a popular view point with many local people.

Four main **objectives** were set for the woodland:

- to provide an attractive and well designed Community Woodland for access and enjoyment by local residents
- to produce good quality hardwood and softwood timber
- to enhance the landscape
- to create and improve wildlife habitats

Design

With these objectives in mind the woodland was designed around a network of paths allowing a variety of circular routes of varying lengths. Included within the path network are a number of benches, a picnic table, welcome boards and a small car park and litter bin.

The main hardwood timber species is oak, with significant amounts of ash, beech, sycamore and gean. The main softwood species are sitka spruce, European larch and Scots pine. Other species were planted for landscape and conservation purposes such as silver and downy birch, aspen, alder, willow, rowan and crab apple. Woody shrubs such as dogwood, guelder rose and holly were also planted to provide wildlife cover and a variety of colour and texture. For added interest a number of large growing specimen trees such as copper beech, lime, horse and sweet chestnut have been planted around the car park and picnic areas. The wood comprises of a mixture of 40 % broadleaved species, 40 % conifer species and 20 % open ground for paths and view points.

The layout of the wood was divided into three main areas. The lower ground to the north of the Kelly burn has been planted predominantly with

Eamonn Wall & Co., January 1996

Figure 1 Lawhill Community Woodland looking east, and the proposed landscape plan.

Figure 2 Lawhill – a view westwards – down the Devon Valley.

broadleaved timber species planted in an intimate mixture of 3000 trees per hectare (1.8 m spacing). This spacing is close so that future timber quality will be improved as a result of side branches being suppressed. A block of Douglas fir has also been planted in the sheltered south west. As well as being an excellent timber tree, Douglas fir is of local interest as David Douglas who discovered the species originated as a gardener in the Valleyfield estate near Dunfermline.

The second area along the burnside is a mixture of open ground and native riparian broadleaves designed to provide 40 % dappled shade to enhance the burn ecology.

The third area on the slopes of Lawhill is predominantly coniferous with a variety of sitka spruce, larch and Scots pine, 5 % birch has been mixed through to provide visual and ecological variety while helping to nurse the spruce during their early years.

Community Involvement

The local community has played a key role in the project. Local interests and opinions were sought during the planning phases by contacting organisations such as schools, youth groups and community councils. Questionnaires were placed in local shops and schools and Civic Trust presentations were given. The local schools were involved in helping to plant some of the trees, and the Drystone Wall Association helped to restore the boundary wall by the car park. The official opening was well attended and consisted of a site tour followed by lunch at Arndean House courtesy of Col. and Mrs Stewart. The day was well attended by the Dollar public and local media and over £100 was raised for Tree Aid, a charity supporting community tree planting projects in Africa.

Current Management Issues

Since the wood was planted a year ago, managements has mainly involved the control of woodland pests such as voles, rabbits and roe deer, and weeding. Pest control obviously requires sensitivity and careful planning to avoid conflict with the visiting public. However, the heavy access pressure and numerous dogs help to discourage unwelcome pests.

Conclusion

The Lawhill Community Woodland project has been successful in meeting its first objective with the site already gaining a high number of regular local visitors. The removal of grazing pressure has led to a flourish of wild flowers with a carpet of bluebells appearing along the burnside pointing to its woodland past. As the trees begin to grow, other ecological changes will take place and regular visitors will notice new plants and birds beginning to make their home at Lawhill.

Obviously it will take time for the woodland to make a contribution to the local landscape, however, much has already been achieved, for which Col. Stewart and the people of Dollar can be justifiably proud.

Notes

Near Lawhill is the Muckhart Community Woodland planned and managed by E. Wall and illustrated in the FNH volume 17 pp15-21 paper by A. Seaman 'Woodlands for the Community'.

LAWHILL COMMUNITY WOODLAND

Come and explore the new 24 acre community woodland at Law Hill, just outside Dollar. 20,000 trees have been planted with paths, benches, viewpoints, a picnic table and a car park provided for your enjoyment. The owner, Col. Stewart, and designers, Eamonn Wall & Co. will give a guided tour and be on hand to answer any questions. Following the tour, soup and sandwiches will be served at Arndean House.

Advert/Poster.

ALL WELCOME

EAMONN WALL & CO.

WOODLAND DESIGN AND MANAGEMENT

Tel: 01259 743212

Lawhill – young oaks coming to leaf.

Figure 4.

BOOK REVIEWS/NOTES (Naturalist)

Forth Estuary Forum (FEF) – promoting the wise and sustainable use of the Forth.

The Forth Estuary and Firth from the river's tidal water limit at Stirling to the Isle of May at its North Sea entrance, is 96 km long and covers an area of some 1700 km². It is a major focus for industry, commerce, transport and recreation. However many of the activities that make the Forth so important can also be damaging to its long term future. Increasing demands on space and resources make it crucial to find a balance between the interests of people and commerce, and the protection of the natural heritage.

The Forum is a voluntary partnership, comprising members from diverse organisations, including industry and commerce, local government, recreation and conservation bodies, as well as interested individuals. It is helping to secure that vital balance, and achieve sustainable economic development for the area.

The Forum has been directed by government to put in place a Management Strategy by the end of 1998. The survey/review work undertaken by its ten Topic Groups has been done and the Forum is now at the important stage of integrating the various issues and recommendations that each Topic Group has documented. The discussion paper *The Forth: The Way Forward* for an integrated management strategy, is now being made available widely, offered as an opportunity for discussion and decision making at all levels, so that solutions which meet local needs can be constructed.

The reports of the ten Topic Groups –
> Awareness and Education
> Built and Archaeological Heritage
> Coastal Defence
> Economical Development
> Fisheries
> Information and Research
> Landscape and Amenity
> Marine and Coastal Pollution
> Nature Conservation
> Tourism and Recreation

include a wealth of information and discussion supplemented by a comprehensive computer database 'Forth Information System' linked to the Internet to take advantage to today's technology in making the information widely available to promote the effective management of all aspects of the Forth in a sustainable fashion.

The Forth Naturalist and Historian and the University of Stirling are members of the Forth Estuary Forum.

L.C.

BOOK REVIEWS/NOTES (Naturalist)

Man and the Landscape Symposium.

The 23rd annual in this series on 20th November 1997 was on *Transportation – People and Environment.* There were seven presentations on historical, current and environmental aspects of walking, cycling, cars, canals, trains and the oil industry, and their impact on the countryside and wildlife. Summary notes on the presentations made by members of Clackmannanshire Field Studies Society (CFSS) have been published in *CFSS Newsletter* no. 60, April 1998.

As noted in *FNH* volume 19, 1996, pp142-3, CFSS have published brief notes on nearly all of these symposia in the April issue of the *CFSS Newsletter* since the first event in 1975. Reports on the November 1996 symposium on *Environmental Awareness and Education* were in *CFSS Newsletter* no. 58.

The November 1998, 24th symposium, is on *Woodlands – past, present and future,* with eight presentations and displays by leading individuals and organisations – touching on some historical (post 1500) and current aspects of native woodlands and their management.

Butterflies for the Millennium. Proceedings of the Scottish Regional Meeting (1997). Editor R. Fox. 1998. 23pp.

Organised by Butterfly Conservation and the Institute of Terrestrial Ecology, Biological Records Office and held in the Smith Art Gallery and Museum, 1 November 1997 – a loan copy is available from L. Corbett.

Papers include – Recording needs in Scotland, P. Kirkland; How SNH uses the data, D. Phillips; Butterfly recording in Scotland, R. Sutcliffe; Recording in remote areas, S. Moran; New Millennium project and progress, J. Asher.

Environmental Information in Scotland: Where do we go from here? Proceedings of a seminar on 21st February 1997 at the National Library of Scotland, edited by Morag Nisbet. 36pp. £10.

Includes:
SEPA activity over its first year – Sargent.
Role of Information in enabling citizen action in environment – Baxter, FOE.
Environmental information needs – Amyes.
A National Environmental Information Centre – Jevens, ENFO, Dublin.
Notes on the Scottish Environmental Information Network – SEIN.

Available on loan from L. Corbett.

L.C.

THE WALLACE OAK, TORWOOD and ROY'S MILITARY SURVEY

Colin D. I. G. Forrester

The Military Survey of Scotland conducted by William Roy in the years 1747-1755 (1) following the Jacobite Rebellion of 1745, was the precursor of the Ordnance Survey, and mapped the whole of Scotland in colour. The 'fair' copy was to the scale of one inch to 1000 yards, and concentrated on features of the terrain of use in military manoeuvers, such as mountain slopes, rivers, roads, boggy lands, fields and buildings. It has been thoroughly described by Skelton (2), and there was a critique of it in 1986 (3).

There is an extra and unusual feature of this great work – William Roy was deeply interested in antiquities and mapped ancient ruins, Roman camps and similar places, and in 1793 he published his researches in his *Military Antiquities of the Romans* (4). Research for my official history of Clan Forrester (5) lead to studying Roy's maps, particularly on Torwood, a small Royal forest in the parish of Dunipace, for which the Forresters were Heritable Foresters to the Stewart Kings from "beyond the memory of man", according to old charters. Torwood has many associations with great figures and episodes in Scottish history, e.g. it was the gathering place for the Scottish army before the battle of Bannockburn, and of Charles II's stand against Cromwell at Torwood Castle.

Of special interest was the intent to discover the possible site of the legendary historic tree, the Wallace Oak, in whose interior the great Scottish patriot and Guardian of Scotland, Sir William Wallace of Elderslie, is said to have hidden after defeat at the nearby Battle of Falkirk on 22nd July 1298 in the War of Independence. The tree was very famous in its time and much visited. Sir Walter Scott referred to it in his *Tales of a Grandfather*, and in *Waverley* he spoke of the Torwood as "glorious to the recollections of the Scottish peasant for the feats of Wallace".

The tree itself was said to have had a girth of 22 feet when measured four feet from the ground, and when largely cut down, some 42 feet girth. There are various reports of souvenirs made from the wood of the tree e.g. Scott himself presented a snuffbox to George IV on his state visit to Scotland in 1822; a box containing wheat from the Antonine Wall elegantly worked in gold was presented to the Prince Regent in 1812 by the Royal Watchmaker of Falkirk (6); the present Queen has a similar box at Frogmore House in Windsor (7); and the Earl of Buchan sent a snuff-mull to George Washington the first president of the United States. The remains of the tree were eventually cut down about 1779, and thereafter its site has been largely forgotten, even locally, until these researches by the author.

Various accounts of the Wallace Oak were noted in parish and county histories, letters and other documents (8-16). While none of these descriptions was sufficient in itself, their combination built up a detailed picture of the tree and its possible location. A number of features recorded for the site could be considered as identified – viz. it was said to be a) in low lands; b) on a slight 'hillock' or swelling in the ground; c) surrounded by marshy or boggy lands of wet clay soil; d) being in the Lower Torwood, later called Woodside or Glenbervie; e) having a road nearby passing through the wood; f) near to another famous tree, the so called "Cargill Thorn" – this was said to be two miles north of Larbert, in the land of the Blairs, in a square field enclosed by a ditch, near Torwood Glen, and east of the main Stirling to Edinburgh highway. Under it the Covenanting field preacher Donald Cargill publicly excommunicated King Charles II and others in 1680. The Wallace Oak is also said to have been approached by a rough stone "Druidical causeway" which then circled round it. But none of these accounts, and others, were clear enough, and to some extent they conflicted with one another, so that a resulting site could not really be decided on. However, while the Torwood area of William Roy's map (1 and 17) was being examined in the British Museum, a significantly peculiar feature was noticed in a conventionaly marked 'woods' area north of the Stirling to Edinburgh road, indicating the remains of the Torwood. Inside this area (Figure 1) was noticed a small yet clearly defined feature resembling a round-topped tree, accompanied by its 'shadow' to the right. The curator of the Map Library agreed that this could be considered to represent an isolated tree, and in view of Roy's known interest in antiquities it seemed likely that this could be the Wallace Oak. William Roy's surveyors worked at speed, using primitive techniques for triangulation, and concentrated on features of importance to a military campaign, sketching in much else by eye. Now, whatever alignment was used, the wood and the 'tree' on the map fell in an area now called significantly, Wallacebank Wood – owned by Glenbervie Golf Course, and formerly a private estate with various owners, including Russell, Darroch, and Carron Iron (16 and 18). A more precise site resulted when an alignment of the main roads was used, in conjunction with the sites of Torwood Castle, and the Tappoch Broch, an Iron-Age stone tower on a hill top. The tree then fell on the edge of that little wood.

The Map Library of the National Library of Scotland then located an estate plan of Woodside or Glenbervie, by William Crawford, dated 1830 (18). On this plan the outline of Wallacebank Wood was virtually identical to its shape on modern maps (Figure 2). Here on this estate plan a later hand has added a pencilled cross and the words "Wallace Oak" (Figures 3 and 4). Neither map by itself would have proved the location, the estate plan could have recorded a later tree misidentified as the original. But the two documents supported each other to within the accuracy of William Roy's triangulation methods. Examination of the plans, and correspondence with W. F. Howie, then a director of the golf course, confirmed the possible site. It agreed in several points with the earlier accounts – to the north was the land of the Blairs, where the Cargill Thorn used to stand; it was on lower land than the remainder of the Torwood; that land had been waterlogged and was of boulder clay; there was a private road within the estate crossing through Wallacebank Wood; the wood itself was on slightly rising land which reached its summit within the wood. It was accepted that this was likely to be the true location, and the *Scotsman's*

James Johnson ran a short feature on the discovery (19) and a slightly fuller account was published in the *Scottish American* (20). There was an attempt made by the author to arrange for an engraved stone to mark the site, but this was postponed as being more appropriate in 1998, the 700th Anniversary of the first battle of Falkirk. Whether the legend of the Wallace Oak has substance is uncertain. Such a tree might have existed in the time of Wallace, though forestry experts have considered it unlikely to have been this 18th century oak (21); though mid 12th century trees have been recently evidenced to early 19th century (22). Nonetheless the Wallace Oak and its site are of historic interest.

The author has also used Roy's map to study the development of the lands and village of Corstorphine, Edinburgh, former territory of the Chiefs of Clan Forrester. The plan of this village, though minute, is impressively accurate when enlarged and compared with slightly later plans, and with the modern layout of remaining streets and houses. A set of such comparison plans has been deposited in the Map Library of the National Library of Scotland.

These modest successes might encourage others to investigate and use Roy's *Military Survey*, now available as coloured slides. It was made in three forms, a) the 'fair' copy of northern Scotland at one inch to the mile, b) an unfinished reduction at one inch to 4000 yards, and c) the *Original Plan of the South of Scotland*, with no fair copy. There are distortions, due to the crudity of the surveying techniques. Terrain was more important than accuracy of outline, but the relief hydrography and the land cover were plotted accurately for their military importance. The river courses and roads were also accurately surveyed. There were conventions for field boundaries; water features were in blue; woodlands conventionally marked in green; moors in buff; and grey washes in various tones for relief. Houses were coloured solid red, with thin red outlines to formal lands, and roads in brown. The symbol for moorland is the usual modern one, and there is stippling for sand and shoal. There are clearly defined limits of cultivation and waste, for enclosed and unenclosed land, for drained and undrained, and for woodland and open country. The map is elegant, detailed, and an amazing cartographic achievement for its time as evidenced in Skelton (2).

References, Notes, Sources

1. W. Roy, Military Survey of Scotland, British Library – London (copies in Edinburgh as reference 17 below).
2. R.A. Skelton, The Military Survey of Scotland 1747-1755. Royal Geographical Society, Special Publication no. 1 1967; reprint in *Scottish Geographical Magazine* 83 (1), April 1967.
3. G. Whittington and A.T.S. Gibson. The Military Survey of Scotland. A Critique. Historical Geography Series no. 18 1986.
4. W. Roy, Military Antiquities of the Romans in North Britain, 1973.
5. Colin D.I.G. Forrester. The Forresters, a Lowland Clan and its Lands. Gronow Press, 1989, pp20-30.

6. W.R. Mcpherson. John Russell (1745-1817) Watchmaker and Clockmaker of Falkirk. *Calatria* 9, 85-96.
7. Julia Harland, Assistant to the Surveyor of the Queen's Works of Art. pers. comm. 3 June 1985.
8. John C. Gibson. Lands and Lairds of Larbert and Dunipace Parishes. 1908.
9. Wallace's Tree in Torwood, in Local Antiquarian Notes and Queries, by Lowe published by the *Falkirk Herald* 1927, p55.
10. Sir John Lauder of Fountainhall. Some Historical Observes of Memorable Occurrents of Church and State from October 1680 to April 1686. Bannatyne Club, Edinburgh 1840, pp44-5.
11. William Nimmo. The History of Stirlingshire. 3rd edition. 1880. volume 1, p 98-9.
12. Samuel Lewis. Topographical Dictionary of Scotland. London. 1846, volume 2, p555.
13. F.H. Croome. Ordnance Gazetteer of Scotland, Caxton. 1903. volume 1, p1574.
14. The Statistical Account of Scotland. 1792, Stirlingshire volume, Larbert and Dunipace Parish, p 557.
15. The New Statistical Account. 1845, volume 8, pp348-9, 381-2.
16. Glenbervie Golf Club. Souvenir Booklet, Golden Jubilee, 1932-1982. 26pp
17. National Library of Scotland, Edinburgh, Maps c9b, sheet 6 2/2 colour slide 111146.
18. William Crawford. Plan of the Estate of Woodside, the property of James Russell, Esq. 1830. MS.NLS Deposit 240, Russell and Aitken Papers. Many of the pencilled comments are said to have been made by James Aitken Darroch, who acquired the estate in 1899; but the site of the Wallace Oak was probably marked around 1850 by Anne Stirling of Glenbervie, whose daughter Mrs Houston of Johnstone claimed in 1908 to have identified the site of the Oak. (Keeper of Manuscripts, NLS, Patrick Cadell, pers. comm. 3 May 1985)
19. James Johnston. Scot uncovers historic tree in family roots. *Scotsman* 8 April 1985.
20. Colin D.I.G. Forrester. Finding the site fo the Wallace Oak in Torwood. *The Scottish American* 5 (3), 1987.
21. W.E.S. Much, University of Edinburgh, Forestry and Natural Resources pers. comm. 22 February 1985.
22. T.C. Smout, editor Scottish Woodland History. Scottish Cultural Press. 1997 (reviewed in *Forth Naturalist and Historian*, volume 20).

Further Reading

R. Oliver, OS Maps: a Concise Guide for Historians 1993.

Editorial Notes

1. This paper was submitted to the *Map Collector* and to *The Forth Naturalist and Historian* in 1992, but publication has been delayed by the author's illness. The author accords acknowledgements to - W.F. Howie, Ann Ross of Southhampton University, Gordon Miller of Torwood Castle, and Walter Gardner for topography and history of the Torwood area.
2. With more information becoming available, and 1998 being the 700th anniversary of the Battle of Falkirk with Wallace's survival of it and the possible relevance of the Wood thereto, a supplementary paper is intended.
3. Wallacebank Wood, owned by Glenbervie Golf Club, is a restricted access Nature Reserve managed by the Scottish Wildlife Trust.

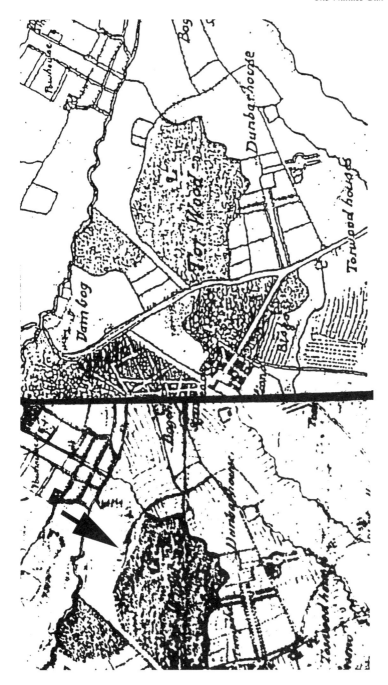

Figure 1 Left – Roy's original of Torwood that shows the 'the tree'.
Right – clarifying enlargement by Forrester showing 'the tree' with shadow to the right.

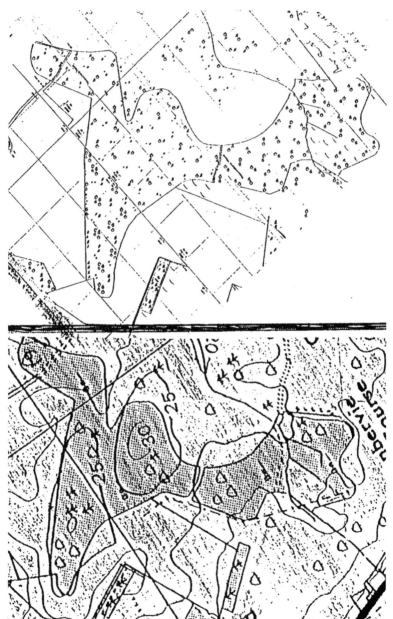

Figure 2 The shape of Roy's Torwood 'wood' in modern maps.

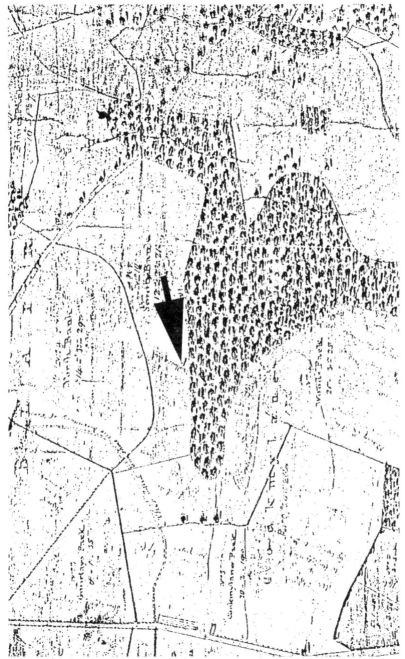

Figure 3 The wood of Figure 2 as in the 1830 Woodside Estate Plan – with the pencilled Wallace Oak location.

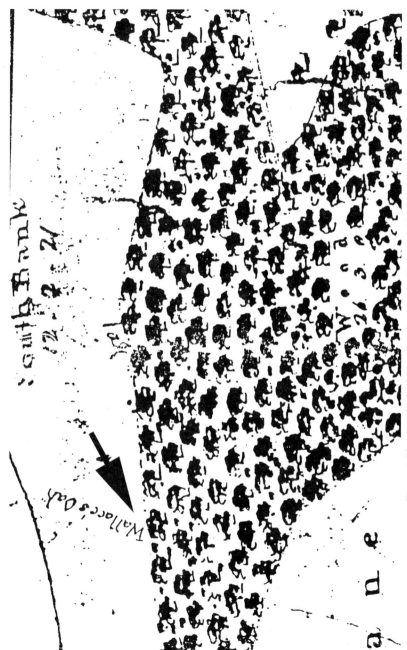

Figure 4 The pencilled Wallace Oak location, enlarged and highlighted.

JAMES WATT'S SURVEYS AROUND STIRLING

Richard L. Hills

Beginning in 1766 until early in 1774, James Watt (1736-1819) was occupied principally in trying to develop a career as a civil engineer in Scotland. In the Stirling area, he was involved through Charles, Ninth Baron Cathcart (1721-1776), at two different periods in various surveys for canals and for improving river navigations. With Robert Mackell, Watt proposed a canal to carry coal from somewhere near Sauchie to Alloa. This may have been surveyed in the spring of 1767. Then in July 1767, Watt carried out his first independent survey for a canal to make the River Forth navigable past Stirling over to Loch Lomond and then to the Clyde at Dumbarton. That August or September, he made another survey to make the River Devon navigable. In 1770, he gave up his experiments on his own new type of steam engine in order to supervise the construction of the Monkland Canal. These schemes for improvements around Stirling were revived in the autumn of 1773, and, although the canal over the Bollat Pass to Loch Lomond was dropped, making the River Gudie or Goodie Water navigable was added. These notes and records from research on Watt's surveys include comments on their background and on people, particularly Lord Cathcart.

The Rivers Forth and Devon

From Aberfoyle on the edge of the Highlands, the River Forth follows a winding course past Gartmore across flat peaty lands until it reaches a weir at Craigforth about a mile to the north of Stirling, where the tidal stretch ends. As the crow flies, this distance is about fifteen miles but by river is very much farther, probably nearly thirty miles. However, as Sir John Sinclair pointed out in 1799,

> "The fall of the river, in its whole extremity of this parish, through the great moss, to Stirling, is very inconsiderable; and the ground consisting almost wholly of moss and clay, is easily wrought".(1)

In fact, the river at Aberfoyle is only about sixty feet above sea level and the fall from Gartmore to Craigforth about thirty feet. The river was described as deep and slow moving but there were shoals where the depth was only a couple of feet.

Below Stirling and beyond Alloa, the tidal stretch of the Forth is also extremely twisting and, in places, shallow. "The distance from the quay of Alloa to ... the bridge of Stirling is 19½ miles; whereas the distance by land ... does not exceed seven miles"(2). There was a quay at Stirling which coastal vessels could reach, often with great difficulty, and, at spring tides, those which could lower their masts to pass under Stirling bridge, could get as far as the weir at Craigforth. There all goods had to be transhipped into very small boats which could make their way up the Forth, being dragged over the fords and shoals.

The region to the north-west of Stirling seemed to present great potential for development. There was slate at Aberfoyle and limestone had been found at Gartmore (3). Agricultural improvement was all the rage at this time, although the various reports about navigation make no mention of it. An improved river would have assisted with drainage of the moss or peat lands. Lord Kames, who entered into the possession of the Blair-Drummond estate in 1766, did improve part of the area near Monteith and straightened the Goodie Water (4). Improving the soil with lime was another aspect of agricultural development. If the navigation could be developed, then coal could be brought up more cheaply from the collieries around Alloa both for making lime and for household fuel. This was where the River Devon became important.

The River Devon rises to the north of the range of the Ochil hills. It starts by flowing north, then turns east before it again turns in a south-easterly direction to reach the Crook of Devon. In a sudden bend, it then heads more or less west towards Stirling, following the foot of the Ochils, but at Menstrie twists again due south to reach the River Forth at Cambus, a couple of miles west of Alloa. In the latter part of the eighteenth century, the streams flowing off the Ochils into the Devon would power many textile mills (5), but in the 1760s, this industry did not yet exist. However there was exploitation of mineral deposits in these hills, such as the Airthrey silver mine in 1761.(6) But these mineral deposits proved to be disappointing in their extent and alone would not have justified making the River Devon navigable.

In its course along the foot of the Ochils, the River Devon follows a geological fault line, and beneath the relatively flat lands to the south, stretching down to Alloa and the Forth, are large deposits of coal at quite shallow depths. This is the western end of the coal-field running through Culross and eastwards into Fife (7). Coal had been mined here from at least 1519 and, by 1640, there were extensive workings in the Clackmannan and Sauchie districts. Much was shipped both around the Firth of Forth and further afield to the Netherlands and the Baltic principally through the port of Alloa where a Custom House was provided in 1710 (8). This coal was described as "the finest … in all this country … and has always been held in the highest estimation, on account of its superior quality"(9).

The principal landowners around Alloa in the 1760s were the Erskines of Mar and Lords Cathcart and Kennet. Around 1730, Sir John Erskine had canalised part of the Devon in order to carry his coal to the banks of the Forth from where it could be more easily despatched to market (10). He achieved this partly by improving the channel of the Devon and partly by installing sluices at "Tilli Body Bridge", presumably a form of flash lock (11). This canal could not have been functioning in the 1760's when Lord Cathcart wanted to extend the exploitation of the deposits at his Sauchie colliery. This mine was very ancient and at this period was drained by an engine which took its water from the River Devon, probably a waterwheel operating lever pumps.

Charles Schaw, Ninth Baron Cathcart

Lord Cathcart was born at Edinburgh in 1721. He succeeded to his father in

1740 and, on the death of his maternal grandfather, Sir John Schaw, inherited his estates which included Schaw Park, the estate of Sauchie in Clackmannanshire, as well as the Schaw estates in Renfrewshire where the town of Greenock was situated (12). Cathcart was an important political figure, being a Lord of the Bedchamber and aide-de-camp to HRH the Duke of Cumberland at the battle of Fontneroy in 1745. As well as continuing his military career, he held many high positions in Scotland such as that of Lord Commissioner of Police between 1764 and 1768. In the latter year, he became Ambassador to the Court of St. Petersburg until 1771. He died in London after a long illness in August 1776.

Greenock, where James Watt was born in 1736, formed a crucial link between Cathcart and Watt. James Watt senior was an important figure in the town where he was a baillie for a number of years and knew Cathcart well. In an age of patronage when whom you knew was probably more important than what you knew, it looks as if Lord Cathcart took the opportunity to advance the career of the young Watt through his position as a Commissioner of Police. Cathcart employed Watt both before and after his time as ambassador in Russia. The Board of Police was established in 1714 with a First Commissioner, five Lords, three Gentlemen, a Secretary, cashier, solicitor and doorkeeper, paid by the English Treasury. It was intended that they should help to improve the government in Scotland and at first had the duty of making proposals on various topics such as the exercise of Crown patronage in the Kirk, reducing the Highlands to tranquility, maintaining the poor, repairing the highways, encouraging the export of naval stores from Scotland, etc. However membership became a comfortable sinecure and the Commission was finally disbanded in 1782 when its records were lost (13). Yet it seems that Lord Cathcart may have tried to revive it because he used it to support at least three of the surveys carried out by Watt.

The Forth and Clyde Canal

Lord Cathcart was involved with the promotion of Scottish canals certainly as early as 1764 when he asked John Smeaton for further information about parts of his report on the project for making a navigable canal between the firths of Forth and Clyde (14). The suggestion for such a canal can be traced back at least to the autumn of 1726 when Alexander Gordon carried out a survey (15). The next step was in 1762 when Lord Napier of Merchiston employed Robert Mackell and James Murray to survey a line from the River Carron to the Clyde about five miles below Glasgow (16). As a result of this, in the following year, the Board of Trustees for the Encouragement of Fisheries, Manufactures and Improvements in Scotland asked John Smeaton to make another survey. His long and careful report was dated 1 March 1764 (17). Smeaton replied to Cathcart's queries on 22 December 1764.

Smeaton's preferred route left the Firth of Forth near the Carron Ironworks and followed the River Bonny westwards before crossing the summit to the River Kelvin. This route would have served Glasgow with a branch canal and entered the Clyde further down at Yoker. He had also made a quick survey of a more northerly route. This would have followed the Forth past Stirling, nearly up to Aberfoyle before striking south-westerly across the Bollat or Ballat Pass to the Endrick Water and so down to Loch Lomond. To gain the Clyde, it would have used the River Leven as far as Dumbarton. The climb up to Bollat, 222 feet above the high water of neap tides in the Clyde, passed through difficult country and one of Smeaton's maps shows that water would have to have been brought from quite long distances to keep the summit level supplied.

Because both these routes by-passed Glasgow, the tobacco merchants there commissioned Robert Mackell in December 1766 "to examine whether there might not be found some track, which, though it was higher, might be shorter, and which should fall into the Clyde nearer Glasgow" (18). Mackell looked at routes through the Monkland area which would enter the Clyde to the east of that city. During February 1767, he was certainly assisted by James Watt (19). It seems that this was Watt's first major canal survey and together they published their report, *An Account of the Navigable Canal, Proposed to be cut from the River Clyde to the River Carron* (20). They recommended a canal 24 feet wide but only 4 feet deep, which would be suitable for small boats but not coasting vessels. Hence its opponents referred to it as a "ditch, a gutter, a mere puddle" (21). When James Watt junior was writing his father's obituary for the Encyclopaedia Britannica in 1820, he confused this scheme with that for the Forth and Lomond passage (22).

Watt was asked to go to London to assist with the passage through Parliament of a bill for this "ditch" canal. He set out on 10 March 1767 and stopped at Brighouse three days later where he looked at some locks being constructed on the Calder Navigation which Smeaton "proposed to make … better than most of the locks he had seen on any river in England" (23). This was most likely the first time that Watt had seen any canal under construction and it would leave a profound impression on his later schemes. The drawings of these locks preserved at the Royal Society in London show well piled foundations and massive stone work for the walls. Watt made notes on the construction and costs as well as the time it took for a boat to pass through. He wrote, "A boat took 12 minutes to pass a lock but was only 8 minutes in the lock. the boats travel 30 miles a day" (24). This visit showed him the great costs of constructing a locked canal, with its need for skilled masons to build it and subsequently adequate water supplies to operate it, as well as the extra costs of maintenance and the time spent in passing barges.

Watt's next visit showed him a different type of canal. He crossed the Pennines to Manchester where he set out for Worsley and travelled back on a boat on the Duke of Bridgewater's canal. At Worsley Delph, he would have seen how coal was brought out of the mine in containers on small boats. A crane transhipped the containers onto large barges which took them along a level canal to Manchester where another crane unloaded the containers and placed them on horse-drawn carts for distribution. While bridges and aqueducts such as that at Barton were still necessary, such a dead level canal avoided the need for reservoirs and major supplies of water as well as expensive lock construction. The Bridgewater Canal could have been the source of inspiration for many of Watt's later canal schemes in Scotland, including some for Lord Cathcart. Watt remained in London until May when the bill for the "ditch" canal was withdrawn. On 1 May 1767, a subscription had been opened for what would become the Forth and Clyde Canal, capable of accommodating sea-going vessels. The Act for this canal received the Royal Assent on 8 March 1768 (25).

The Lomond Passage

In the meantine, there was an abortive attempt to revive the idea of a canal up the Forth and by the Lomond Passage. In July 1767, Watt received instructions from Lord Cathcart to carry out a further survey of this route.

> "Instructions for Mr Watt
> Mr Watt will herewith receive a copy of James Morrisons report of the passage from Alloa to Dumbarton through Lough Lomond.
> James Morrison will meet Mr Watt as soon as he can go to Dumbarton from whence they will proceed in the Tract described in the Report to Alloa; they will examine the same and give their joint opinion upon it specifying any observations and amendment that may occur to them illustrated with proper Plans & sections of such alterations" (26).

James Morison was an English land surveyor who had come to Scotland to find work. He used an address at Alloa and so may have been known to Lord Cathcart and may have carried out other work for him. He also surveyed routes for canals through the Great Glen and the River Gudie but for whom it is not known. His survey of the Lomond Passage was carried out for the Commissioners of Police (27). Morison later would work with Watt on many of his other surveys, including that of the River Devon for Lord Cathcart. For Watt to be asked to comment on Morison's route, it is possible that we have an instance of the Scots wanting the work of an Englishman checked by a person from their own country whom they could trust.

Smeaton's survey of the Lomond Passage was very brief, so it can be understood why Lord Cathcart wanted a more detailed one. Morison's report was not finished and given to Lord Cathcart until that July (28) and contained no estimates of costings which was one of the points Lord Cathcart wanted to know. In his report (29), Morison gave the length of what would become the Forth and Clyde Canal as $28\frac{1}{2}$ miles of artificial cuts and the distance from its westerly end to Dumbarton as eight, making a total of $36\frac{1}{2}$ miles. The Lomond Passage, including $6\frac{1}{2}$ miles in the lake itself, would be 47 miles. But the Lomond Passage, while climbing about 40 feet higher, had fewer artificial cuts, so Morison wrote,

> "Upon these principles in point of time there cannot be great difference betwixt the two passages. The one being shorter and more uniformly certain at all times, the other being readier by having fewer locks; but the Lomond passage must cost

less than the Carron passage and for that reason as well as from the addition of the natural commerce of the rivers Forth and Leven which would be very considerable may in all probability afford an equal profit to the undertakers at a much lower toll" (30).

Watt's notes show he left Dumbarton on 20 July and passed through Drummond, Bucklivie, Alloa and over to Falkirk. As well as Morison, he took some of his 'lads', a term he used for the journeymen in his mathematical instrument business. No doubt these lads were employed not only in helping with the surveying apparatus but also in ascertaining the nature of the ground through which the canal would pass by digging holes and using boring rods. They returned to Dumbarton on the 29th. They covered much the same ground between August 7 to 11th. On October 5th, he received "from the police £35.0.0, & my Expenses £7.10.0, the lads £3.12.0 (31).

They looked particularly at the summit over the Bollat where Lord Cathcart thought a tunnel might be better than a cutting. Cathcart must have heard of the tunnel at Harecastle for the Trent and Mersey Canal because he wrote,

"It has been found in England that it is better to pierce than to surmount, & in the great Staffordshire Navigation they conduct it 2½ miles under a mountain, estimating the drift at £5,000 per mile" (32).

Watt thought that the canal could be lowered 20 feet through this pass but that a tunnel would be impracticable. To supply the summit level with water, he followed Smeaton's proposal of taking water from the higher reaches of the Endrick Water and constructing a reservoir of 60 acres at Burghmore. To take this water to the Bollat Pass, an aqueduct 4½ miles long would be necessary. Here we discover another of Watt's ideas. He proposed to carry the line of this aqueduct over narrow gullies in wooden troughs, presumably similar to those which carried water to waterwheels (33). He would develop this idea into canal aqueducts.

Cathcart later sent Watt instructions about writing his report in which he could follow Morison's, commenting on that one section by section. Watt was to compare his suggestions with Smeaton's original report, except that his canal would be 8 feet deep. Watt's calculations were to be "founded on real particulars & on principles which you will explain" (34). Watt's report was much longer than Morison's and was presented in three sections covering from the Clyde up the Leven to Loch Lomond, from Loch Lomond over the Bollat to the Forth at Offering and finally the Forth itself as far as Craigforth mill and dam. To make the River Leven navigable would require three locks to overcome a difference in height of just over 19 feet (35). This section, a distance of 5½ miles, would cost £6,575.18.11 (36). To surmount the climb up to the Bollat Pass, 19 locks would be needed, followed by a similar descent of 17 locks. These locks would be 18 feet wide, 64 feet long, 10 feet fall, with 7 foot 6 inches of water for boats of 60 to 70 tons. This section was to be 13 miles long, costing £60,386.10.7 (37). The Forth itself was to be shortened from 30 to 22 miles by means of cuts, although Watt doubted whether some of Morison's cuts were necessary and he recommended leaving more of the route in the existing river bed. Three locks were to be built at the shallows or fords. This section was estimated at £12,766.13.7 3/4, giving a total for a canal from the Firth of Forth to the Firth of Clyde at £79,729.3.1³/₄ (38). The extra cost of lockage over the Bollat Pass will be noted.

The Tidal Forth

Watt made more journeys to the Stirling area in August and September in conjunction with surveys of the tidal stretch of the Forth and the River Devon. His survey of the Forth below the weir at Craigforth appears to have been undertaken to check on Morison's work and complete the route of the Lomond passage. A glance at a modern map will show just how twisting this river still is and how navigation would have been improved by straightening it. There was also the problem of a shoal called the "Thrask" between Alloa and Cambus, where the River Devon joined the Forth. Watt took soundings in the river on 21 September 1767, "Being two days before the full moon" (39). If cuts were made and the river deepened, vessels of 100 tons might go all the way to Stirling every spring tide without fear of lying on the shoals. To reach Craigforth higher up, he recommended cutting a canal to by-pass Stirling bridge so that masts need not be lowered. A swing bridge at the northern end of the present bridge would accommodate passenger and road traffic. The total estimate for the work was £5,333.17.3¹/₂, while shortening the river and reclaiming the old bed would gain 237 acres valued at £5,925 (40).

The River Devon

There was nothing exceptional in these reports for the Lomond Passage or the Forth, but it is in Watt's proposals for the River Devon that we first find originality with schemes for level canals without lockage. Morison had surveyed the higher reaches of the Devon about Sauchie in 1765 (41), and, possibly as a result of this, Lord Cathcart sought Smeaton's advice in February 1766 (42). Smeaton was at Cambus quay on 20 November 1766 when he must have looked at the tidal Forth as well but his report on the Devon is dated 14 September 1767, nearly a year later, which may be another reason why Cathcart asked Watt to make a survey. Smeaton's report mentioned a scheme by Robert Mackell and Watt

"of carrying a canal upon a dead level from Tillicoutery to a point opposite the schoolmaster's house at Alloa, following the foot of the rising grounds the whole way, and which will be about 30 feet higher than the sea, proposing to continue the same from thence between banks across the flat ground to the waterside (which is not far), or making a cut through the flat grounds to the dead level termination of the canal, which plan would save locks and waste of water, I can only say, that from my view of the country, I believe such a project practicable; but, as I have neither plans nor sections of the course that it would take, I am in no capacity to judge of the expence.

"It is obvious that this canal would be defective in not suffering the vessels to pass into the Forth, and that either the banking across the valley, which would be a considerable depth, would be a considerable article of expence; and that in any view of the affair, if a communication with the Forth is dispensed with, a considerable saving may be made, but I apprehend not above 1-3d..."(43)

Unfortunately Watt's surviving papers give us no clues about his survey or the estimates for this canal. We can only assume that he and Mackell made it during the end of May or June 1767 after they had returned from London. Presumably it was meant to carry coal from Lord Cathcart's mine at Sauchie to the port of Alloa. It would have taken a shorter route than following the Devon but it is impossible to compare the savings made by having no locks with the greater expence of higher embankments or deeper cuts. This is Watt's first scheme for a dead level canal on which goods would be transhipped into and out of small barges. Hence this would have been a narrow canal, cheap to construct, but not suitable for sea-going vessels. Watt's suggestion was clearly based on the Bridgewater Canal and he would propose this concept again for some of his other schemes in Scotland. The line of this canal may have been made partly redundant in 1766 or 1768 when one of the earliest Scottish wooden waggon ways was built by John Earl of Mar from the Waterwheel Pit to the docks at Alloa (44). Later this waggon way was extended further into the coalfield and presumably made any canal redundant.

Lord Cathcart's correspondence with Smeaton on 5 November 1767 (45) also mentions a survey of the River Devon carried out by Watt. This must have been made that August or September, possibly in conjunction with the survey of the tidal Forth. Cathcart may have been trying to extend the sale of his coal up the Forth itself into the region beyond Stirling, and, if so, this could account for Watt's suggested line of this canal. Watt realised that the mill dam at Menstrie, where the Devon made its last southerly turn to fall into the Forth at Cambus, was on the same level as the weir at Craigforth above Stirling. Therefore he proposed making a canal to carry the line of the River Devon further westwards towards Stirling, to pass round the foot of the hill where the Wallace Memorial now stands, cross the River Allan either by damming that river or by an aqueduct, and meeting the Forth just above Craigforth weir. This scheme would give level water almost from Alva, where Lord Cathcart's colliery lay to the south, as far as Frew, about two-thirds of the way up the Forth towards Offering and Aberfoyle. In essence, here was another of Watt's dead level canals, avoiding the delays of boats locking into and out of the tidal Forth giving a good route for Cathcart's coal into wider markets. This might have provided a cheaper and safer alternative than improving the river itself.

In this scheme, Watt proposed the first of his wooden aqueducts in order to make a low level crossing of the River Allan. Cathcart realised the difficulty of constructing a masonry aqueduct with little clearance for floods and for which expensive foundations would be necessary, rendering the expence enormous. Smeaton commented,

"It is executed in wood, upon the plan of Julius Caesar's bridge, which is well adapted to resist ice, or other floating bodies, or upon any better more modern construction, it is apprehended it would come much cheaper, would stand against the force of the stream, and of the ice in the winter, and would not be affected by the land floods, which cannot rise to the sole of the aqueduct, but must be liable to the expence of repairs to which a stone bridge would not be subject" (46).

Later, Watt would suggest a wooden aqueduct for the Bo'ness Canal which was never built and another for the Campbeltown Coal Canal. For this second canal, he sent drawings to his friend Charles Macdowall in 1782 and the likelihood is that this one was built on the Kintyre peninsula. Smeaton was very guarded in his reply about the aqueduct and canal, pointing out that, if the purpose of this canal were only to link the Devon collieries with the upper Forth, then Watt's scheme "seems very well adapted for that purpose, and in that case would merit serious consideration" (47). However, if coal were to be sent down the Firth of Forth, then he could not see that ships would pass up the tidal Forth and then back along the canal. Watt's report for this improvement to the Devon at this time has not survived. All these schemes must have been abandonned when Lord Cathcart left to take up his post as Russian Ambassador in 1768.

The Surveys in 1773

Lord Cathcart returned from Russia in 1771 (48) but it was not until the end of the summer in 1773 that he asked Watt to commence surveying for him again. This may have been due firstly to the failure of the Ayr bank in June 1772 which caused an economic crisis in Scotland and secondly to Watt's employment as Resident Engineer building the Monkland canal until at least May 1773.

Watt received his instructions to carry out a quick survey for a 'Northern' canal through the great Glen from Lord Cathcart on behalf of the Commissioners of Police. He left Schaw Park with Morison on 1 September 1773, leaving behind in Glasgow his first wife, Margaret, who was ill and pregnant. At Fort Augustus on 25 September, Watt heard that his wife was seriously ill. He left Morison to complete the survey and hurried south, not knowing that Margaret and their fifth child had died the previous day (49).

For most of that October, Watt tried to console himself with experiments on telescopes and barometers and, after Morison's return towards the end of the month, drawing part of Loch Ness. But, just before Morison came back, Lord Cathcart wrote on behalf of the Commissioners of Police to Watt to encourage him after his loss. He suggested that Watt and Morison should survey "the Tract from the lint miln at Menstry on ye Devon to the upper Forth & give your opinion respecting a canal to join those rivers and respecting the navigation of the upper Forth" (50). The tidal Forth below Stirling was to be included as well. Watt arrived at Schaw Park on 3 November and left the next day for the lower part of the Forth for what would prove to be his last survey for any navigation. Except for three Sundays spent at Schaw Park, Watt was surveying the Forth for the whole of November and, after settling accounts with Morison on 5 December, sent an abstract of his report to Lord Cathcart on 7 December (51). The report was printed by 17 December and corrected the following day (52). John Golborne was also asked to carry out a survey that November and sent a four page report on the Forth below Stirling, commenting that "it has almost every defect possible" (53) but also saying that he needed better weather to carry out a proper survey.

It seems that Lord Cathcart must have been principally interested in improving the transport for coal from his colleries. Watt was asked whether there should be a lock for shipping at Craigforth or whether a navigable canal should be built to some port lower down the river. Cathcart also wanted a report about making the "Goodie Water" navigable from the Forth to Menteith which Morison had surveyed in April 1769 (54). To make the Gudie navigable would mean passing the mills of Thornhill and Cardross and straightening the course of the river. For the Forth and Devon, Watt seems to have recommended his earlier scheme of a canal from Menstrie to Craigforth to avoid navigating the difficult lower reaches of the Forth. This time, there were locks to avoid making an aqueduct over the Allan. Otherwise, he followed his earlier reports of 1767. Above Sauchie, the canal would have to be raised 20 feet by three locks and a separate channel to reach the collieries higher up-stream around Coalsnaughton which would take it at least to Mallack Foot (55). The canals would be 16 feet wide at the bottom and four feet depth. The locks were to be $13^1/_2$ feet wide, 72 feet in length so that the boats on the Forth which were 56 to 60 feet long and 13 feet wide could be accommodated. The cost for "Rendering Navigable the Rivers Forth & Devon" was £13,040.13.6 (56).

This scheme seems to have been favourably received by Lord Cathcart at first and he wrote to Watt on 7 December,

> "I had yesterday ye pleasure of reading your summary & conclusion to my friends at ?Tillibody? & have ye satisfaction to assure you that they commend it much so you may rest satisfied it will be well received by others" (57).

Cathcart made some comments about the Devon above Sauchie which are illegible so it is evident that he must be referring to Watt's report on the Forth and Devon and not the 'Northern' or Caledonian Canal. But soon after this, Cathcart must have received an alternative report, possibly from Morison, who recommended a saving of £4,147 by terminating the canal from the Devon at Queenshaugh opposite Stirling and transhipping at Craigforth which would avoid the expensive locks. A shorter alternative was to end the canal a little lower down the Forth at Manor Pow which would avoid the Thrask. This was certainly Morison's suggestion (58).

Watt stuck to his original proposals but one wonders what was his reaction to Morison submitting a rival scheme. Also harsh comments were to follow from Lord Cathcart. Once again he must have been referring to Watt's Forth & Devon report and not the 'Northern' canal when he wrote on 9 January 1774,

> "I have lately read two reports of Mr. Smeaton's; I think his manner very concise clear & satisfactory & a good model for such compositions: your report is most incorrectly printed which I am persuaded you will attend to in future publications" (59).

Again there must be speculation about the effect of this letter on Watt from his main patron. Part of Lord Cathcart's anxiety may have derived from the proximity of a meeting in Edinburgh to be held on January 12 about obtaining a Bill in Parliament for the Forth & Devon scheme (60). Watt was in Edinburgh from January 8 to 22, possibly with Morison, when he had a further report printed in which he modified his suggestions (61). He returned to Edinburgh again from January 27 to February 4 about the Forth and Devon (62). On 31 January, there was a meeting when £4,500 was subscribed (63).

Lord Cathcart wrote to Watt on 14 February that there were problems with the Forth & Devon bill and on 9 March that there was lack of support for it (64). Cathcart also commented,

"I am not surprised at the bad account you give me of poor Morison's map. It is very desirable to employ people of one's own country but I am much afraid it must be allowed to be better in the lights of certainty despatch & [word illegible] to bring in artists from a distance. I am sorry your headaches still continue and have so long retarded your Report of the Northern Canal" (65).

Did Watt take this as a warning? Many of his own reports, such as that for the Commissioners of the Forfeited Estates for a canal between Loch Gilphead and Crinan, had been long delayed and it seems that he had acquired a reputation for being dilatory. He may have felt that Lord Cathcart would turn to others for surveys in the future.

This must have been the period when Matthew Boulton was pressing Watt to go to Birmingham where his steam engine could be built at Boulton's Soho Manufactory. Watt's surveying career was not proving very profitable because he had not been paid for much of his work, including that for the Forth and Devon. In the middle of May 1774, he packed up his things, left Glasgow on the 16th. and arrived in Edinburgh a couple of days later. Here he met Lord Cathcart who "was satisfied with my Account of Survey of Inverness Canal" (66). There had been no meeting about the Devon Canal since Watt was last in that city so he left Edinburgh without being paid. Watt arrived in

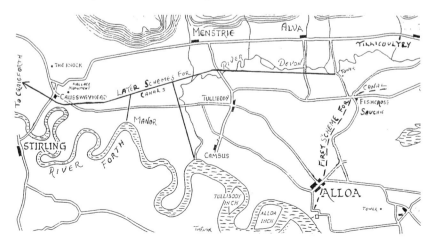

Birmingham on 31 May, never to live in Scotland again. His future brother-in-law, Gilbert Hamilton, tried to obtain payment in December 1775 with no success (67) and arguments with Morison over parts of the accounts continued into October 1776 at least (68). Lord Cathcart died in August 1776 after a long illness (69) so the chief protagonist for making the rivers Forth and Devon navigable was no longer there to give his support. In any case, by that time, the wooden waggon way was beginning to be seen as a cheaper alternative for collieries to transport their coal to the staithes for shipment by sea and neither of these rivers was ever made navigable.

Acknowledgements

I would like to thank the archivists and librarians at the Birmingham Central Library, the National Library of Scotland, the Scottish Record Office, both in Edinburgh, and the Stirling Record Office for their help in the preparation of this article. Travelling to research in these places would not have been possible without a grant from the Royal Society, London, to whom I wish to express my thanks also.

References, Notes, Sources

1   Sir John Sinclair, Ed., *The Statistical Account of Scotland, 1791-1779, Vol XII, North and West Perthshire*, (reprint Wakefield, 1997), p. 16.
2   P. Graham, *A General View of the Agriculture of the Counties of Kinross and Clackmannan*, (Edinburgh, 1814), p. 211.
3   Birmingham Central Library, Boulton & Watt Collection, [B. & W. Col.] Muirhead Papers [M] I 3/7d, James Watt's Report, Description of the River Forth from Craigforth New Miln to Alloa Shore, 21 Sept. 1767.
4   *The Farmer's Magazine*, Monday, 4 August 1817, pp. 261 and 263
5   Brian A. Park, *The Woollen Mill Buildings in the Hillfoots Area*, (Forth Naturalist and Historian, 1984).
6   *Mines and Minerals of the Ochils*, Clackmannanshire Field Studies Society, 1974, 2nd ed. reprinted with corrigenda, 1994, p. 5.
7   Ian Bowman, Coalmining at Culross 16-17th centuries, *Forth Naturalist and Historian*, 7, 84-125, 1984.
8   A.I.R. Drummond, *Old Clackmannanshire*, (Alva, 1953), pp. 15-6.
9   Sir John Sinclair, *The Statistical Account of Scotland, 1791-1799, Vol IX, Dunbartonshire, Stirlingshire & Clackmannanshire*, (reprint Wakefield, 1978), p. 160.
10 Sinclair, *Dunbartonshire*, p. 161.
11 *Reports of the Late John Smeaton, F.R.S., made on various occasions, in the course of his employment as a Civil Engineer*, (London, 1812), vol i, p. 142.
12 Sir James Paul, Ed., *The Scots Peerage, founded on Wood's Edition of Sir Robert Douglas's Peerage of Scotland*, (Edinburgh, 1905), vol ii, p. 520.
13 P.W.J. Riley, *The English Ministers and Scotland, 1707-1727*, (London, 1964), pp. 185-7 and A. Murdock, *The People Above: Politics and Administration in mid-Eighteenth Century Scotland*, (Edinburgh, 1980), p. 20.
14 *Smeaton's Reports*, Vol II, p. 56.
15 Jean Lindsay, *The Canals of Scotland*, (Newton Abbot), 1968, p. 15.

16 Ibid, pp. 15-6.
17 A.W. Skempton, Ed., *John Smeaton, F.R.S.*, (London, 1981), p. 113. This date is given by Charles Hadfield but I cannot find any date printed in *Smeaton's Reports*, vol ii, p. 31f. However Morison gives this date in his report, see B. & W. Col., MI 2/40.
18 Lindsay, op. cit., p. 160.
19 B. & W. Col., MI 2/4, Cash Memorandum Book of James Watt.
20 National Library of Scotland, Ms. 5.3651 (19), *An Account of the Navigable Canal, Proposed to be cut from the River Clyde to the River Carron, as surveyed by Robert Mackell and James Watt*, (London, 1767).
21 Lindsay, op. cit., p. 18.
22 Birmingham Central Library, James Watt Papers [JWP] 3/26, p. 8c, original text of J.Watt junior's obituary of his father.
23 Skempton, op. cit., p. 105.
24 B. & W. Col., MI 2/4.
25 J. Priestley, *Historical Account of the Navigable Rivers, Canals, and Railways, throughout Great Britain*, (reprint Newton Abbot, 1969), p. 266, 8 Geo. III, C. 63; Royal Assent, 8 March 1768.
26 B. & W. Col., MI 3/36, 7 July 1767, Ld. Cathcart to J. Watt.
27 B. & W. Col., MI 3/10, J. Morison's Report to the Lords of Police on the Lomond Passage with J. Watt's comments added at the end.
28 B. & W. Col., MI 2/40, J. Morison's *Report upon a Canal from the Forth to the Clyde by the Lomond Passage*, July 1767.
29 Ibid.
30 Ibid.
31 B. & W. Col., MI 1/14, J. Watt's Note Book.
32 B. & W. Col., MI 3/36, 7 July 1767, Ld. Cathcart to J. Watt.
33 B. & W. Col., MI 3/8a, J. Watt's Report on the Lomond Passage from the Forth over the Bollat Pass to Loch Lomond.
34 B. & W. Col., MI 3/43, 24 ?August? 1767, Ld. Cathcart to J. Watt.
35 B. & W. Col., MI 3/9, J. Watt's Report on making the River Leven navigable from Loch Lomond to the Firth of Clyde.
36 B. & W. Col., MI 3/8.
37 Ibid.
38 Ibid.
39 B. & W. Col., MI 3/7a, J. Watt's Report on the Lower Forth past Stirling up to Craigforth and T. Crouther Gordon, James Watt's Bold Plan for the Devon, *The Alloa Journal*, 3 Sept. 1960.
40 B. & W. Col., MI 3/7c.
41 JWP 3/22, J. Watt's rough draft of his report.
42 *Smeaton's Reports*, vol i, pp. 154-161.
43 Ibid, Vol I, p. 161.
44 J. Adamson, *Sauchie and Alloa, A People's History*, (Clackmannan, 1988), p. 5 and M.J.T. Lewis, *Early Wooden Railways*, Routledge & Kegan Paul, (London, 1970), p. 255.
45 *Smeaton's Reports*, vol i, p. 147.
46 Ibid, vol i, p. 148.
47 Ibid, vol i, p. 149.
48 Paul, op. cit., p. 521.
49 B. & W. Col., MI 1/20, J. Watt's Journal.
50 JWP 4/10.19, 24 Oct. 1773, Ld. Cathcart to J. Watt.
51 B. & W. Col., MI 1/20.
52 Ibid.

53   JWP 3/69, from J. Golborne, in collection of *Reports to the Lords Commissioners of Police, relative to the Navigation of the Rivers Forth, Gudie and Devon, 1773.*

54   JWP 4/33.1 & 2, 23 & 29 April 1769, J. Morison to J. Watt.

55   JWP 4/82, 7 Dec. 1773, J. Morison to J. Watt.

56   B. & W. Col., MI 2/81, 13 Jan 1774. J. Watt, *An Account of the Scheme for Rendering Navigable the Rivers Forth & Devon, with Estimates of the Expence,* Printed 1774.

57   JWP 4/82, 7 Dec. 1773, from Ld. Cathcart to J. Watt.

58   JWP 4/10.10, 6 Jan. 1774, Ld. Cathcart to J. Watt.

59   JWP 4/10.9, 9 Jan. 1774, Ld. Cathcart to J. Watt.

60   JWP 4/10.18, 28 Dec. 1773, J. Callander to J. Watt.

61   B. & W. Col., MI 1/20 and JWP 3/22 *Report on the Rivers Forth & Devon,* 18 Jan. 1774, also printed in J. Sinclair, *General Appendix to the Statistical Account,* vol i, pp. 369-380.

62   B. & W. Col., MI 1/20 and MI 2/42, *Expenses on Surveys,* etc., 1769-1773.

63   B. & W. Col., MI 1/20.

64   JWP 4/10.6 & 7, 14 Feb. and 9 March 1774, Ld. Cathcart to J. Watt.

65   JWP 4/10.6, 9 March 1774, Ld. Cathcart to J. Watt.

66   B. & W. Col., MI 1/21, J. Watt's Journal.

67   JWP 4/20.24, 11 Dec. 1775, G. Hamilton to J. Watt.

68   JWP 4/33.21, 27 Oct. 1776, J. Morison to J. Watt.

69   Paul, op. cit., p. 522, Ld. Cathcart died on 14 August 1776.

Note

Five or six years ago, the remaining private papers of James Watt were purchased for the nation and deposited at Birmingham Central Library. This enabled the Revd Dr Richard L. Hills to base his research for a fresh biography of this important Scottish engineer on all the archive material which is likely to become available. These collections comprise those of the personal papers of James Watt, the Muirhead and James Watt Papers, those of his partner, Matthew Boulton, the Boulton Papers and those of the partnership, the Boulton and Watt Collection. The Heritage Lottery fund has just announced a grant of £400,000 towards conserving and cataloguing this mammoth collection which is the most important of its type in the world covering the Industrial Revolution.

The research carried out by Dr Hills covers many areas of Watt's life never investigated before. This includes Watt's career as a civil engineer, and hence his work in the Stirling area. Unfortunately for this there are no surviving maps drawn by Watt himself; hence the sketch map accompanying this article. Watt's contributions to medical science will be covered at a conference in Edinburgh this August with a talk on Watt's experiments on gases for Dr Thomas Beddoes and the Pneumatic Institution, Clifton, near Bristol. It was hoped that tuberculosis might be cured by breathing something like oxygen but of course this proved illusory.

HARVEY'S 'LOST' CHILD RESTORED

Maria Devaney

A painting by Scottish artist Sir George Harvey (1806-1876) which until recently languished in store as an unidentified oil on panel, has been recognised, restored and put on display.

The Smith Art Gallery and Museum has a collection of over seventy oil sketches by Harvey, who was born in St Ninians near Stirling in 1806. His father was a clockmaker, and the family moved into the town when Harvey senior was admitted into the Hammermen's Trade. His business premises were at 80 Baker Street. Most of the collection of sketches was gifted to the Smith by the artist's niece, Ellen Harvey in 1935, after she discovered them in a folio, and rescued them from Harvey's old studio in Regent Terrace, Edinburgh.

Art historians familiar with the work of George Harvey easily recognise and connect the sketches with some of Harvey's famous finished paintings, for example, *The Covenanters' Preaching* (Glasgow Museums), and *The Covenanters Baptism* (Aberdeen Art Gallery and Museum). Many of the Smith's collection of sketches relate to some of Harvey's 'lost' paintings, including *The Small Debt Court* (exhibited 1833) and *The Lost Child Restored* (exhibited 1829). These early works document the life and people of Stirling in the early part of the 19th century. The Smith has four oil sketches of figures relating to *The Lost Child Restored*. The connection between these sketches and the unidentified oil was made while studying the Harvey collection in preparation for an exhibition. The figure sketches for the *Finder of the Lost Child*, the 'Aunt' carrying a tray of drinks, and the 'Mother', when compared with the oil on panel, clearly replicate the figures seen in the finished painting, slightly modified by the artist.

Curators at first believed the oil to be a copy of Harvey's original image for *The Lost Child Restored*, since no documentation seemed to link the painting directly with Harvey himself, but further investigation and research into the 1935 gift from Ellen Harvey, has now convinced them that the formerly unidentified oil, is indeed Harvey's original composition for *The Lost Child Restored*. Ellen Harvey's original gift consisted of seventy oil sketches, restored by her friend William Walker ARE. The collection was exhibited at the Smith for the first time in 1938, and accompanied by a guide written by Miss Harvey. The printed guide notes later gifts to the Smith from Miss Harvey including the initial composition for *The Lost Child Restored*. The Smith has not always been fortunate enough to have professional curators in post during its chequered history. This has led to such information being lost. The Smith Institute as it was originally known, opened in 1874, was requisitioned by the War Office during two world wars, and endured a further period of neglect when the building fell into disrepair and was nearly demolished in the 1970's.

The small oil on panel measuring 402 x 580 mm, was recorded as merely 'Interior Scene' by an unknown artist, until the identification was made. It shows a middle class Stirling family at home. At the centre of the image the 'lost child' is being held by his mother. The grandmother of the runaway boy scolds him, while the young aunt hands round a tray of drinks. The finder of the lost child is seated with a stick in one hand, while he gestures the story to the mother. His own boy is behind, helping himself to the drinks, while a black servant enters the room at the rear. According to Ellen Harvey, her uncle was fascinated by the subject matter of the 'lost child', and she suggested that his early sketch books revealed a variety of try outs. The Smith's oil sketch for the 'Finder' shows how the artist experimented with hand gestures – the man has three hands. Ellen Harvey also mentions that the artist prepared two oil paintings on the same subject, the other one (still missing) featured the father of the lost child, counting notes to reward the finder, as an alternative to the scolding granny. The Smith also has the figure sketch for the father.

As soon as the identity of the oil on panel was discovered, curators decided to have it restored and put on display with the related sketches. It was restored earlier this year by Clare Meredith at Hopetoun House.

Study for Mother and Child.   Study for the Aunt.

Both oil on paper by Sir George Harvey.

The Lost Child Restored. Oil on Panel. Sir George Harvey.

BOOK REVIEWS/NOTES (Historical)

Stone Age Alpha. Edward Paterson. Ruthven Press. 1998.

The author of *The Message of Scotland's Symbol Stones* claims his researches on Megalithic burial sites show that religious beliefs of the indigenous people can be traced from a very early period and were not just Latin and Greek myths and legends introduced by the pagan Romans. The early pious Christian clerics in Britain and Ireland built our Christian Faith upon the foundation of the customs and rituals of our early forebearers.

Blind Harry's Wallace. William Hamilton of Gilbertfield. Luath Press. 1997. 260pp. ISBN 0-946487-33-2. £7.50.

Originally published in 1508 by Chepman and Myllar of Edinburgh, and titled *The Actes and Deidis of the Illustre and Vallyeant Campioun Schir William Wallace*, it had gone through over 20 editions before Hamilton, a soldier and poet of the Glasgow area, presented it afresh in his contemporary English. As such it influenced many, and until this 1997 book, it went through over 20 editions again till the last of 1859.

Long out of print, now Elspeth King, who knowledgeably introduces this handsomely produced work, has striven nobly to ensure it is again available. It is a work which has influenced notable writers from Burns and Scott, on to Randolph Wallace from the American south, the writer of the novel and the film *Braveheart*. The typographically attractive text is intriguingly annotated; and nicely illustrated by Owain Kirby of Stirling.

Elspeth King describes this as a landmark opportunity for mature reflection on how Scotland has been shaped, and she sees *Blind Harry's Wallace* as an essential and compelling text to this end.

The Archive Photographs Series by Chalford Publishing, Stroud, Gloucestershire.

Working with local historians, archivists, groups and museums this series aims to create new photographic histories of towns and cities around Scotland. This year published titles in this *Images of Scotland* series will include Falkirk, Bo'ness, The Trossachs, Kirkliston, Broughty Ferry, Irvine, Melrose and North Glasgow. Central Glasgow was published in 1997. Compiled by Peter Stewart, 129pp. £9.99.

L.C.

THE LEGEND OF ROBERT KIRK
RECONSIDERED

Louis Stott

The Reverend Robert Kirk (1644-1692), the seventeenth century minister of Balquhidder and of Aberfoyle, is known about all over the western world because of his interest in fairies. If he did not invent fairies, he has a strong claim to have been one of the first to have written down, in his book *The Secret Commonwealth*, what he thought he knew about them. Yet when a leading Scottish newspaper celebrated the tercentenary of his birth, the local minister was quoted as expressing the hope that Kirk's connection with fairies would be forgotten about, and that his work giving Highlanders access to the Bible would be remembered. Indeed, Kirk's achievements in this field are equally remarkable, yet, until recently, Kirk's grave was neglected, and his image is frequently distorted. Anywhere else in the world the possession of such an icon might be made more of.

Perhaps, you may say, this is just as well, and the visitor can find out for her, or himself, about Robert Kirk. Furthermore, it might be supposed that everything that can be found out about the Reverend Robert Kirk has already been discovered. However, some aspects of Kirk, apparently taken for granted, deserve re-examination.

Kirk, the seventh son of the Rev James Kirk, was born in Aberfoyle on 9th December, 1644. He became the minister in Balquhidder in 1664, and eventually succeeded his father in Aberfoyle in 1685. He was the reliable and well-regarded clerk to the Synod of Dunblane from 1667 until 1688. His lifetime was a period of exceptional political and religious upheaval in Scotland: when he was four Charles I, who sought to impose both Bishops and an alien Prayer Book on Scotland, was executed; and, when he was nine, Cromwell's troops, who eventually subdued the whole of Scotland, were defeated in the Pass of Aberfoyle. He lived to see the Restoration of Charles II, both in Scotland and in England; the reign of his Roman Catholic brother, James VII; and the revolutionary succession of William of Orange. During much of Kirk's ministry Episcopalianism was imposed upon Scotland, but Presbyterianism was restored in 1688. Kirk survived these changes when some of his colleagues were driven from their pulpits, persecuted and killed for their beliefs.

Kirk is a highly significant figure. Perhaps his greatest achievement in his own lifetime was to make the Bible accessible in the Highlands of Scotland during these troubled times when even the inhabitants of the parish of Aberfoyle were overwhelmingly Gaelic speakers. An Irish version had been available for some years and it provided the basis for the transliteration which the redoubtable minister then went to London to see through the press. Kirk's Bible was in use for over a hundred years. However, alongside these labours, Kirk collected local folk tales, and made what was among the first scientific studies of the supernatural.

Kirk's interest in fairies ought to be granted more respectability than it sometimes is. Perhaps it would be if his death had not given rise to a curious and dramatic legend: his spiriting away by the fairies, and his re-appearance as a wraith. This story was – quite rightly – emphatically dismissed by his principal biographer, Reverend Professor Donald Maclean, in a paper given to the Gaelic Society of Inverness in 1924, but, in spite of such strictures, it has persisted. It has recently been revitalised by the interest taken in 'close encounters of the third kind', and in pagan beliefs, as an aspect of what is called the 'New Age'. These pseudo-scientific connections distance the scientific community from Kirk, and result in him being regarded as a figure of fun.

In a happy phrase, Cunninghame Graham, in his *Notes on the District of Menteith* (1895) described Kirk as "the astral vicar of Aberfoyle" which carries with it a prophetic hint of this. Nowadays Kirk might be described as an 'abductee', and 'the fairies' might be described as 'aliens'. Kirk's legendary experiences on the 'Fairy Hill' were, perhaps, 'close encounters' with a world we do not yet understand. Indeed, there are curious resemblances between the phenomena described by Kirk and the experiences of 'abductees'.

In a *Horizon* programme [BBC2 28 November, 1994] Professor Michael Persinger, a neurobiologist from the Laurentian University in Ontario, described experiments which he had carried out to stimulate hallucinations in the temporal lobes of volunteers with computer programmes which imitated the brain.

"The experiences which are generated experimentally are primarily the fragments of abduction-type experiences and mystical-type experiences, and even the beginnings of some kinds of psychical or near-death experiences: pleasant vibrations, feelings of being light, leaving the body, perhaps a sense of a presence, also sensations that involve visual experiences – the feeling that it's a dream but it's more intense than a dream – very often the feelings that alter reality, feeling that the self is detached from the body. And sometimes sexual arousal occurs, which is a very important feature, because we find that many of these patterns are very much like the incubi and succubi reports of previous centuries, where people felt a sexual arousal at the time when the entity was visiting them." [Michael Persinger quoted in the adapted transcript of *Horizon*].

This is very reminiscent of Kirk's *Secret Commonwealth*, in which detachment from reality, out-of-body experiences and succubi, for example, are frequent themes. Persinger went on to suggest that the kind of energy-release required to bring about these experiences might be explained by earth movements or earthquakes. Aberfoyle and Doon Hill are, of course, situated on the Highland Boundary Fault. Unfortunately, earthquakes at Comrie, situated on the same fault and undoubtedly the place most associated with earthquakes in Scotland, were not recorded until 1789. However, there was an earthquake in England in September, 1692. Perhaps such earth movements might have taken place along the Highland Boundary Fault when Robert Kirk was 'taken'. Thus Kirk's experiences can be seen as phenomena which continue to recur, which scientists are still seeking to explain, rather than something simply made up.

For his part, Cunninghame Graham, was sceptical. In *Notes on the District of Menteith* he opined that Kirk's fairies were folk-memories of the Picts, "with all due deference to Andrew Lang, the Rev Mr Kirk, and to the members of the Psychical Research Society". His introduction to the Eneas Mackay reprint of Lang's edition of *The Secret Commonwealth* managed to enthuse about the book without necessarily being committed to it.

An intriguing aspect of Kirk's interest in fairies is the number of famous men it brought him into contact with, of whom Robert Boyle is the best-known. Recent studies by Michael Hunter, Professor of History at Birkbeck College, the University of London, have drawn more attention to Robert Boyle's interest in the paranormal. That such an eminently respectable scientist, who was one of the first to identify hydrogen, and whose 'law' is still one of the foundations of modern science, should be interested in the occult might be considered as shocking as an interest in fairies on the part of a minister of religion, but only with hindsight.

Hunter has shown that Boyle was a hypochondriac who used quack potions, and experimented with magic. As has long been known he was a secret alchemist, but it is now seen more clearly that he was also a dabbler in the occult, yet Boyle was also an extremely pious man who spent much of his fortune in making Bible accessible. These interests make the connection between Robert Boyle and Robert Kirk, the Fairy Minister of Aberfoyle, a striking one. Boyle's involvement with Kirk, both of whom were seventh sons, comprehended both the religious and the supernatural. Boyle helped to finance Kirk's version of the Metrical Psalms, and Kirk's Gaelic Bible. For his part Kirk appended a letter addressed to Boyle from George MacKenzie, Lord Tarbat (1630-1714) to *The Secret Commonwealth*. The subject of the letter, written in response to an inquiry from Boyle, was 'Second Sight'. (Boyle's letter, displaying his interest in such matters, was suppressed by Birch, his biographer.) Perhaps as a consequence of Kirk's publication of it, Lord Tarbat's letter was widely circulated , and it was later quoted by Lord Reay, an early member of the Royal Society, in correspondence with Samuel Pepys. Pepy's interest in second sight was 'defence-related': he wondered whether it could provide 'naval intelligence'.

An intriguing aspect of the letter is that Lord Tarbat states that he began to investigate second sight when he was "confined to abide in the North of Scotland by the English usurpers". He had joined the Earl of Glencairn's Rising against Cromwell of 1653-4, which began in Aberfoyle, and involved Graham of Duchray who was later to appear in the story of Robert Kirk in a significant capacity.

It may be difficult for us to appreciate it, but the Royal Society began by investigating both natural and supernatural phenomena. Boyle himself contributed papers at meetings dealing with both. It is part of Professor Hunter's argument that these interests in no way reflect on his qualities as a scientist, or, for that matter, on his piety. Indeed, he reports Boyle's conscientiousness in resisting temptation in relation to the transmutation of metals, and his "strong sense of anxiety about the power that alchemy might unleash". Boyle's confidantes in these matters were Gilbert Burnet (1643-1715), an exiled Scot who became Bishop of Salisbury, and Edward Stillingfleet (1635-99), eventually Bishop of Worcester. Notes which Kirk made when he was in London supervising the publication of his Bible illuminate this aspect of Boyle's life. He had an interview with Stillingfleet who said that occult phenomena like second sight entailed the danger of illicit contact with the Devil on the part of those who indulged in them and were therefore sinful. Stillingfleet's wife, uninhibited by her husband's views, expressed a wish to know more and it was for her that Kirk wrote *The Secret Commonwealth*. Thus Kirk's learning and his 'fairy' scholarship was much more ordinary than has sometimes been acknowledged.

'Second sight' interested both statesmen and scientists in the seventeenth and eighteenth centuries and it tempted Scotland's most famous visitor, Samuel Johnson, to investigate it. Kirk was the first significant Scottish source to describe 'second sight', but two of his fellow countrymen, James Frazer and Martin Martin also described instances of it, and the idea that 'second sight' was associated with the Western Isles rather than with, say, Perthshire became fixed in the public mind and interest in Kirk waned, but it was revived early in the nineteenth century by Sir Walter Scott, abetted by one of Kirk's successors, Rev Patrick Graham. It was at this point that the legend of Kirk's death made its appearance. It has bedevilled Kirk's reputation ever since.

As a piece of folklore the story is an appealing one. Briefly, it tells how Kirk was spirited away by the fairies while walking on a hill near the manse. He later appeared to a relation whom he told to persuade the local laird to attend the baptism of his (Kirk's) posthumous child, and when he (Kirk) appeared to throw a dagger above his head whereupon Kirk would be released from fairyland. Kirk appeared, but 'by some unaccountable fatality' the dagger was not thrown. Thus Kirk is still captive in fairyland. Stewart Sanderson, Kirk's best-informed modern commentator, characterised it as "apt, but faintly ludicrous". Some folklorists have been anxious to espouse it, as if it gave provenance to *The Secret Commonwealth*, rather than, perhaps, distracting attention from the scholarly reputation of the Minister who wrote the book.

Whether it is true in any of its particulars, or not, the legend of Kirk's death has taken on a life of its own. It is frequently all that is known about Kirk, yet on examination the tale is rarely accurately told. The legend is interesting because it is of comparatively recent origin, it is unusually complex, involving a number of different folk elements, and it is continuing to evolve.

The story seems to have originated with Patrick Graham (1750-1832). It first appeared in the 1812 edition of *Sketches of Perthshire*. Scott, in *Rob Roy* [1817], and subsequent authorities including Chambers' *Domestic Annals*, Andrew Lang, Evans Wenz, Lewis Spence, and Katharine Briggs seem to have relied on it. What is interesting about this is that the story did not appear in the first edition of Graham's book, although the learned minister did discourse on various other local superstitions in the 1806 edition. For example, a story about the fairy hill situated north of Loch Chon appears in the first edition. This is sometimes attributed to Kirk's contemporary Martin Martin, but Graham is the source of it. Graham originally produced the notes on which the guide book was based in 1792 for a visit which was made to the district by the famous artist Joseph Farington. He was collaborating with John Knox in producing what would have been one of the first illustrated books about Scottish scenery, but the project was abandoned when Knox died. The 1812 edition of *Sketches of Perthshire* was clearly produced in response to the enormous popular success of *The Lady of the Lake*, and contained a map illustrating the poem. In it Graham inserted the story of Kirk which he prefaced with a reference to its resemblance to the Danish fairy story of the captivity in fairyland of Ethert Brand. This appears in what is called the 'Ballad of Alice Brand' in Canto IV of *The Lady of the Lake*. Scott freely acknowledged that it was from Graham that he obtained a number of the local superstitions which he incorporated in his world-famous poem. Here Graham returned the compliment.

Maclean, Kirk's biographer, suggests that Graham made this story up, and it does contain several inconsistencies. Graham, it was pointed out, unaccountably got Kirk's date of birth, and thus his age, wrong. Maclean quotes the inscription on Kirk's gravestone. On the gravestone at present in the old kirkyard, which was last refurbished between 1880 and 1904 during the incumbency of Rev William Taylor, the date of Kirk's death and his age are given. It seems unlikely that the gravestone was so illegible in Graham's time that he couldn't read it, so why he got this wrong – and confused Scott – is inexplicable. Graham may also have made another important mistake. He stated the Kirk was walking "upon on a little eminence to the west of the present manse which is still reckoned a Dun Sh_.". The 'Doon Hill' which is popularly supposed locally to be the hill on which Kirk was taken is east of the manse, not west of it. Kirkton Hill is west of the manse. It can be added that another hill, still called the Fairy Knowe, and an altogether more likely spot than either, is south of the manse. These two errors on Graham's part may simply be careless mistakes. Furthermore, Graham of Duchray, who features in the story of Kirk, was over ninety years of age when Kirk's child was baptised, and perhaps it is not surprising that a ninety-year-old failed to throw the dagger above Kirk's head. That this should not have been pointed out by Graham can be characterised as slipshod, but this omission, together with the errors, suggest that he did not take the story very seriously.

Scott took his information about Kirk from Graham and compounded his mistakes in *Rob Roy*. An illustration of the way in which things get distorted is that in early editions of *Roy Roy* the note about Kirk states that he appeared to a 'medical' relation of himself and of Graham of Duchray. Graham's version was a 'mutual' relation, altogether more understandable. However, it is Scott's misprint which has most often survived in the telling of the tale.

Lewis Spence analysed Graham's narrative, and drew attention to the similarities which there are between it and fairy stories about mothers-in-milk being taken by the fairies, and other folk tales surrounding childbirth. Kirk's wife was pregnant when he died, and Spence suggests that it is understandable that, in these circumstances, some of these folk-beliefs were transferred to him. Spence's conclusion is that the story of Kirk's death contains a number of elements from a variety of folk tales. It is not difficult to see how Kirk's known interests in 'fairies' might have led local people to surround his death with various stories of this sort. Of these, one, not relayed by Graham, attaches to Kirk's grave. One might suppose that if Kirk was kidnapped by the fairies, they would have left a stock, indistinguishable from Kirk himself, and that his 'body' would have been buried. However, it is sometimes said (e.g. as reported by Evans Wenz) that his coffin was filled with stones which would have been quite unnecessary. With an empty sepulchre, and Kirk's later re-appearance at the baptism, the story beings to bear an uncomfortable resemblance to the Resurrection. This addition to the story can safely be dismissed as a fabrication.

In her authoritative *Dictionary of British Folk Tales* [1971] Katharine Briggs rather oddly chose to use Andrew Lang's account of Kirk's death. Lang's introduction to *The Secret Commonwealth* puts Kirk into context, referring, for example, to such topics as psychical research and to folk-tales from elsewhere in the world, but his telling of the tale of Kirk's death is very much second hand. Katharine Briggs appended her own contribution to Kirk's legend. She told Stewart Sanderson, in a private communication, that she met a young woman in Methven in 1943 who was expecting a baby:

> "She ... was anxious to get back to the Manse before it was born, for the local tradition was that, if a baby was born in the manse and christened there, Kirk could be freed from fairyland if a dirk was thrust into the seat of his chair..." [Penguin Dictionary of Fairies]

Katharine Briggs told Stewart Sanderson that she believed that this was only 'whimsical belief on her part'. In other words it was simply a significant example of the longevity of the legend. As a result of an inquiry from an American correspondent I recently investigated this story locally. Two features of it are inaccurate: the Manse was not let during the War, it was occupied by the Minister and his family; nor was there a chair there supposed to have been Kirk's. It seems likely that the young woman concerned was the wife of an officer billeted in Manse Road. Her baby was born in Aberfoyle, and was baptised Robert.

The most recent addition to the legend is an encounter with Kirk reported by R.J. Stewart in *Earthlight*. This took place in 1982, and it is described by Stewart in terms which permit the reader to interpret it as personal spiritual experience. Stewart is a serious student of such phenomena who has written a number of books, and is well-regarded in his field. He describes visiting Doon Hill where he found himself "communicating with someone – was a short man, fairly plump, who declared himself to be Robert Kirk". An unkind explanation would be that there were two eccentrics on the hill that day. Stewart goes on to describe how Kirk invited him to join him in fairy land, and how he came to his senses when he heard the sound of a car horn. In the book he describes his experience in a way which allows that he may simply have fallen asleep. He subsequently produced a modern edition of the *Secret Commonwealth*. Strikingly, he did not mention his own experience of Kirk in that book.

Pious ministers have long been properly interested in the beliefs of their parishioners, and in recording them. Kirk's *Secret Commonwealth* is one of the earliest surviving documents of this sort. It is thus a precursor of the many collections of folk-tales of the Highlands and Islands which have been made since. Yet Kirk's interest in the spiritual – both in what might be perceived as evil spirits and in the Christian religion – is perhaps, difficult for us to comprehend nowadays. He has always interested folklorists; and successive generations of them have descended on Aberfoyle to visit his grave. It is when he seems to be an apostle of the occult, asserting that there is 'evidence for 'second sight', and for the existence of an alternative society of 'subterraneans' that difficulties arise. His pious successors have sometimes asserted that such beliefs are best dismissed.

It might be better to appreciate Kirk as a remarkable man of his times.

Short Bibliography

Graham, Patrick. 1806. *Sketches Descriptive of the Picturesque Scenery on the Southern Confines of Perthshire.* Peter Hill, Edinburgh.

Graham Patrick. 1812. *Sketches of Perthshire.* Peter Hill and J. Ballantyne, Edinburgh; and Longmans, London.

Hunter, Michael. 1990. Alchemy, magic and moralism in the thought of Robert Boyle, *British Journal for the History of Science* 23, pp387-410.

Kirk, Robert (edited S. Sanderson) 1691. *The Secret Commonwealth.* Folklore Society [1976]

Kirk, Robert (edited A. Lang) 1893. *The Secret Commonwealth* – Bibliotheque de Carabas.

Kirk, Robert (edited R.B. Cunninghame Graham) 1933. *The Secret Commonwealth.* Eneas Mackay.

Stewart, R.J. 1990. *Walker Between Worlds.* Element Books.

Stewart, R.J. 1992. *Earthlight.* Element Books.

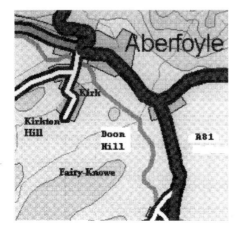

Aberfoyle showing relative position of Doon Hill, Kirkton Hill and Fairy Knowe.

BOOK REVIEW (Historical)

Towards Democracy in Scottish Education. Andrew Bain.

Not a great deal has so far been written about local education during the period of the schools boards of 1873-1919, and what is available about this important time for emerging democracy in school control tends to consider either the predominantly urban or the predominantly rural experience. The present study is a much-needed analysis of what happened in an area of mixed economy during a time of fundamental political and social change in central Scotland.

The main purpose of this detailed survey of some 70 school boards is to consider how economic change was expressed in the social composition of their membership, and to what extent such expression made practical the intention of the Education Act of 1872 to widen the control of local schools. The early chapters analyse the continuing, but modified, influence in Fife education of the landowners, the clergy, and the burgh councils, all of whom had been involved before the Act. The later chapters assess the extent to which the Act's encouragement of other social groupings was translated into their effective representation on school boards.

The detailed analysis of the contribution made by two of these new groupings (women and skilled workers) suggests that some modification will be required in current views: first, about the numbers and participation of women board members in Scotland; and secondly, about the way in which the numerical and effective involvement of skilled tradesmen grew over almost five critical decades. Future general studies of Scottish educational history will have to take account of the wider range of representation reported here and possibly existing elsewhere than Fife.

Copies of this study are available from the author at: 22 Clarendon Road, Linlithgow, EH49 6AN at a cost of £8.75, plus postage and packing of £1.00.

Dr Bain has papers in *FNH* on Education in Bothkenmar (vol. 5), The First School Board of Tulliallan (vol. 18). In 1989 he published a book *Patterns of Error, the Teacher and External Authority in Central Scotland* 1581-186, and earlier in 1965 *Education in Stirlingshire from the Reformation to 1872.*

THE KINROSSES of STIRLING and DUNBLANE
People of the Forth (11)

Lindsay Corbett and John S. Kinross

"Always a razor sharp entrepreneur" is a recorded description of Henry Kinross, coachbuilder to Queen Victoria. The Kinross Royal Warrant coachworks and examples of its products are briefly described and illustrated in Mackay(1909) Lannon (1983), and McCutcheon (1986). He was not the first, nor the last, of the Kinross family to earn that 'entrepreneur' reputation. *The Surnames of Scotland* (Black 1946) lists the name as coming from the lands of Kinross-shire, where for many years from the 12th century on they were landowners and Hereditary Sheriffs. In 1286 John de Kynros attracted the displeasure of Edward King of England ('Hammer of the Scots') by his allegiance to Wallace, and lost for a while both lands and office of Sheriff, but all would appear to have been restored to him and his heirs by King Robert the Bruce by the time of the Battle of Bannockburn.

Kinross not being a numerous name can the more readily be traced, and searches of the archives by Black above, and one commissioned by a John Kinross of Feltham (1934) reveal a long and distinguished history of the name. Kinross/Kynros names occurring in the records include several in the Charters of Inchaffray Abbey; one in which a Henry de Kynros with other nobles and Church dignitaries attests several Charters in the reign of William the Lion c.1201, and witnessed grants to the Abbey of Cambuskenneth c. 1214 (Cambus, 18); one of a Gilbertus de Kinros in 1170 attesting a St. Andrews charter (RPSA, 216); in 1269 is a Writ for payment of 100 shillings to the King's Clerk Thomas de Kynros; in 1280 Henry de Kynros, Archdeacon of St Andrews, helps the Chapter choose a Bishop; in 1290 Sir Thomas de Kinross sold lands in Forfarshire to join Wallace (Roger's *Red Book of Wallace*); a record of 1304 is for a safe conduct for Mathew of Kynros, Dean – and later Archdeacon – of Dunkeld, and later an order for a ransom of £200, for his goings to Rome; and a 1398 notice (CRA, 374) recorded another Gilbertus in Aberdeen. So the records show a number of Kinrosses as Knights, some holding high offices in state and church, being among the Lesser Nobility of Scotland, and possessing coats of arms. Author Kinross has an example of one. Kinrosses appear in records of King William; Alexander III; Queen Margaret; Edward the First, King of England; his sister; and others of the days of Wallace and Bruce.

A traditional story of the 'coachbuilder' family is that one of their 14th century Kinrosses, said to be a wheelwright, had settled in Stirling, and at the time of the Battle of Bannockburn he realised that it would be fortuitous to take part in the winning side. No doubt he was an 'entrepreneur', also like some others of the family, a bit of an amateur actor. He was with the 'small folks army' of locals, yeomen, carriage men, camp and other followers, which armed with warlike implements, banners, flags etc, appeared on the hills at a crucial, if rather late, time in the battle, so making a striking diversion which had such an (intended) impact on the English that they fled the field in belief that these Scottish 'reserves' were a large and powerful force. For his services young John Kinross is said to have been rewarded by Bruce with some land in Stirling. ...Now while there may be no documentary evidence of this family tradition, a reading of A.A.M. Duncan's recent translation and analyses of Barbour's *Bruce* (1375) is interesting. The *Bruce* is the classic epic poem which is the basic source of most writings on Bruce and the Battle of Bannockburn – including Prebble's *Lion in the North* and the National Trust's Guide. Such reading of Duncan suggests that a Kinross just could have been the 'leader/captain' of the 'small folk' at that crucial time of the battle. Quoting from Duncan's Barbour – p49 ... "The King instructed the carriage men, valets and boys, that when they saw the armies engaged they should go with standards made from sheets and clothes, and preceded by trumpets, from the neighbouring wood, (mounted) on carriage horses, so that when the English saw them they would think they were an army ...," and... "did choose a leader ... *(the most interesting part of the story)* ... intent on sharing the loot, but too late to fight." All this was due to Sir Alexander Seton coming from the English side to urge Bruce to attack in the morning as the English "had lost heart....and he would discomfit them without losses" (Barbour p450).

Kinrosses lost the Kinross-Shire lands and Sheriffdom, but possessed the estates of Kippenross and Kippenrait near Dunblane in these times, and on into the 15th, 16th (they were confirmed as a Barony in 1507), to the 17th centuries when they came to possess or repossess the two Dunblane estates, and Auchlochy, and were farming landowners in the Strathearn and Menteith areas, e.g. in the 1590 *Roll of Landlords for Perth Strathearne, Montieth* is listed Kinross of Kippenrait (Register of Privy Council). Black (1946) gives the story of a William Kinross of the latter Menteith area who in 1635 had his plaid and sword stolen by the Macgregors. But in the early 1600s the Kinrosses of Kippenross were in financial difficulties and lost or sold these Dunblane estates, e.g ... Kippenross to James Pearson Dean of Dunblane in 1633. James Pearson in 1646 built a new fortified L-shaped house over the ancient tower house of the Ros family. William Pearson in 1778 sold the Kippenross estate to John Stirling of neighbouring Kippendavie. *A matter of naturalist interest here is that in front of Old Kippenross, extended and modernised over the years, and occupied by the Stirling-Aird family, is a plaque marking the site of The Big Tree of Kippenross – this was the largest plane tree in Scotland, planted in 1400, and in 1842 its girth was 42 feet and its height 100 feet. It was blown down in 1868.* With the Pearsons and the Stirlings of Keir the Kinrosses of this family were involved in disputes of money matters in various law suits. Losing these estates they became tenants of Feddals and other farms in the Strathallan and southern Perthshire areas. So the Kinrosses and relations are basically farming people of these areas; but also in England – in Warwickshire, Middlessex, Stafford, and Windsor areas. In 1852 John Kinross of Gannochan farm in Dunblane parish married Elizabeth Graham Stirling, of another old established farming family of the area. Her grandfather invented the first really practical thrashing machine on the principle of which all modern machines are constructed (Chambers *Domestic Annals of Scotland*). Her uncle was Thomas Graham (1803-69) famed chemist, professor, discoverer of the law of diffusion of gases, and known as the Father of Colloidal Chemistry. He was Master of the Mint from 1855 to 1869, and was the first President of the Chemical and Cavendish Societies. This Elizabeth, Mrs Kinross, was the mother of John Kinross (1934) already referred to. Another relationship was formed by a marriage in 1878 with the Mortons – of the Graham and Morton businesses. Kinrosses are frequently mentioned in Scottish affairs and in holding important offices in Stirling, Perth, Inverness, Edinburgh, and Buckinghamshire.

We come back now to the establishment of the coachworks (McCutcheon 1986). Henry Kinross was an appentice in the coaching business of William Croall in premises in Shore Road when the Croall family withdrew to resite their business in Edinburgh, leaving the company in the hands of Henry Kinross. The business, now William Kinross & Sons, established 1802, developed rapidly and well, and included the innovative introduction of a steam engine, the first in the town. This greatly interested the apprentice Randolph at the time, and he went on to become a noted engineer with his own works in Glasgow, and eventually to the great Fairfield Shipbuilders. By 1838 the Kinross coachworks were so advanced that they were honoured by appointment as – Queen Victoria's Coachbuilder for Scotland – with the Royal Warrant conveyed in letters by Lord Dalmeny (Mackay 1909). The Queen and Prince Albert visited Stirling in 1842, but their route did not encompass the Kinross works. Here again the entrepreneur trait of the Kinrosses was demonstrated in achieving publicity/acclaim by his getting into the cavalcade a huge timber platform on wheels to carry some 70 people. When the railway came to Stirling in 1848 Kinross became a major supplier of railway carriages, and had the works linked to the railway. A disastrous fire destroyed the works in 1850, but such was the success in rebuilding that a genuinely improved street omnibus was entered to the 1851 Crystal Palace great exhibition, and was awarded a silver cup. Founder Henry Kinross was succeeded by his nephew William; the works continued to prosper, and in 1865 moved from Shore Street to Port Street – now the Marks and Spencer building and Thistle Centre entrance area (Figures 7 and 6).

William died in 1874 and his two sons George and James inherited the business – they were sons of his first wife Janet who was killed in 1847 by a run'away farm cart whilst holding the baby James, but she just managed to put him safely on the tailboard. George (Figure 9) became a member of the Town Council in 1879, a Baillie in 1882, and Provost and High Sheriff in 1891. Some notable events in which he played a conspicuous part are recorded by Drysdale (1899); e.g. in August 1882 he presided at the Wallace Monument unveiling of the bust of the Reverend Doctor Charles Roger, the leading promoter of the monument. In December he presented the Freedom of the Burgh to Sir Henry Campbell-Bannerman, MP for the Stirling Burghs, and later Prime Minister (1905-1908). The Campbell-Bannerman statue was erected in

Stirling in 1913. It has been suggested that he may for some be remembered for his rugby connections rather than his politics or the Liberal Party. In April 1895 the Provost was the 'Old Boy' at the annual festival of the High School of Stirling (Graham, 1900). On 24th May 1895 he opened the now (and present) Stirling Post Office, dispatching the first telegram to the Queen, it being her birthday, and the first letter, to Campbell-Bannerman. In 1896 he opened the new filters at Stirling Water Works in the Touch Hills. A silver water jug received on that occasion has been lost. In 1897 he entertained the Franco-Scottish Society, receiving warm thanks from Jean Casimir-Perier, ex-fifth President of France. In September 1897 he chaired the national gathering on Abbey Craig celebrating the 600th anniversary of the Battle of Stirling Bridge, when in the evening the Earl of Roseberry eloquently toasted the "immortal memory of Wallace".

The coachworks flourished (Figures 2 and 4), with its products in great demand at home and abroad – in Europe, India, and even Russia – all types of carriages – all made to order. However, increasingly people wanted to 'see and buy' and it became necessary by 1890 to develop a major showroom (Mackay, 1909), "which will hold its own with anything of the same kind, even in the city of London". Business was still going well through the 1920s – with Lannon "Orders for our Standard cars will be executed in strict rotation". But the mass produced car was now becoming the norm, not special bodies built on basic chassis. So the 'coachworks' developed as a garage business, (see the 1930s advert in the *Observer Annual*, Figure 3), but still producing when required horse drawn lorries/floats through the Second World War, the 150th anniversary in 1952, and on until Marks and Spencer, who had earlier bought the showroom part, wanted to expand in 1966. So ended William Kinross and Sons, Coachbuilders, founded 1802. Its workers were snapped up by Alexanders of Falkirk and other coach works at home and abroad. To date there are no surviving products of the once great Kinross coachworks on display – some are still active no doubt in the coach and horses show field, have been seen at auctions, but not on museum display, though it is understood that there is a coach or coaches in the National Coach Museum of Lisbon. All we seem to have are trade posters/cards/adverts (Figures 1, 2, 3), a commemorative plaque (Figure 5), and a photo of a possible Kinross built delivery float of Reid's Glen Farm Dairy (Figure 8).

As the works, and farming, shrank, members of the coachbuilding, and other Kinrosses, took to emigrating – some to Australia, and one of note – young Cecil (b. Uxbridge 1896) going to Canada in 1913, joined the Alberta Infantry in 1916, fought so bravely at Passchendaele in France on 30th October 1917 that "his superb example and courage" earned him that highest of battle honours, the Victoria Cross (*London Gazette* January 11 1918). He returned to Loughead, Alberta, to farming, till his death in 1957. ...Author John Kinross's grandfather John, RSA,FSA, (b. Stirling 1855, d. Edinburgh 1931, *Who Was Who*), was a prominent architect, and responsible for some grand designs, though maybe few came to be completed. However, he excelled himself in restoring Falkland Palace for the Marquis of Bute; and with Augustine Priory,

St. Andrews; and Greyfriars Friary in Elgin. He designed many houses from 1885 to 1914, including own family ones in Moretonhall Road, Edinburgh, where his parents regularly entertained artists and friends from Europe, including Rodin, Peploe, Guthrie, and Duncan; also other designs e.g. – the Carmelite Friary Church, South Queensferry; Ardtornish, Oban; and Carlekemp, North Berwick. His design for the rebuilding (1903-5) of the 1790s Manderston House near Duns for rich Sir James Miller of Leith, was based on his favourite house, Adam's Keddleston Hall, Derby, and the result is one of the finest Edwardian houses in Scotland.

His son, author John Kinross's father, John Blythe Kinross (b.1904 d.1989, *Who's Who* 1990), business man/financier, was certainly a "razor sharp entrepreneur". The author recalls as a schoolboy on a visit to the seaside, wanting a trip to the lighthouse, being told by a gruff boatman that one man and three children did not provide enough income to make the trip worth while. His father promptly seized the loudhailer and walked around the beach until there were some 40 customers. He then made sure the family had the best seats, and took over the scenery commentary as the boat owner was still recovering from the shock. He was one of the Appeal Sponsors to Industry and Commerce (London) for the founding of the University of Stirling. He founded the Mary Kinross Charitable Trust, which includes Student Houses Ltd, contributed to the First and Third Foundation Appeals of the University, where there is a named John Kinross Wing (Figure 11), a substantial part of the Fraser of Allander halls of residence; and he was at least partially responsible for getting some other contributors of the 'named halls'. The University has a portrait of him by Alan Sutherland (Figure 10). Made an OBE in 1958, he became a CBE in 1967. His Industrial and Commercial Finance Corporation helped fund Lord Fraser to take over the *Glasgow Herald*; he supported much medical research; and published *Fifty Years in the City* in 1982. His obituary is in the *Times* of 25th August 1989.

Members of the family, and relations, have been, and are, associated with Stirling's Allan Park South Church, where a handsome stained glass window of 1937 (Figure 12) commemorates the dedicated services of four Kinross members – William (1852-1901), John (1855-1931), Henry (1858-1916) and David (1863-1936).

So the Kinrosses have earned a place in the history of Stirling, and in our 'People of the Forth.'

Note. In the coachworks photograph (Figure 6), the two men on the left of the doorway were staff of the works – John Booth joined in 1923, and the photo was taken by his aunt who lived across the road, and John Rankine, back to camera, joined in the mid 20s. Both men were from Aberdeen. In the Kinross Building photograph (Figure 11) the man is author John S. Kinross.

Acknowledgements

To Bob McCutcheon for expert advices and information; to Alastair Kinross son of author Kinross, and James Morton, Session Clerk of Allan Park South Church, for family information and assistance; to Stirling Library; and to Stirling Archive.

References and Sources

Barbour, J. 1375. The Bruce, an edition with translation and notes by A.A.A. Duncan. Canongate, 1997, 800pp.

Black, 1946. Surnames of Scotland. New York Library. reprint Canongate, 1998.

Chambers,C. 1874. Domestic Annals of Scotland.

Drysdale, W. 1899. Old Faces, Old Places, and Old Stories of Stirling. Second series. Eneas Mackay.

Graham, J.L. 1900. Old Boys and their Stories. The High School of Stirling. Mackay.

Kinross, J. 1934. Some account of the family of Kinross, Kinros or Kynross. mss.

Lannon, T. 1983. The Making of Modern Stirling. Forth Naturalist and Historian.

McCutcheon, R. 1986. Stirling Observer, 150 years.

Mackay, E. 1909. Industries of Stirling and District. reprint 1998, Stirling Library.

The Times. 1989 25th August 12f. obituary of John Blythe Kinross.

ESTABLISHED
1802.

APPOINTED MAKERS
TO THE QUEEN,
1837.

WILLIAM KINROSS & SONS,

STIRLING CARRIAGE WORKS,

CARRIAGE BUILDERS TO HER LATE MAJESTY QUEEN VICTORIA.

1802.

1910.

DESIGNERS AND MANUFACTURERS OF EVERY DESCRIPTION OF CARRIAGE FOR USE AT HOME OR ABROAD. SPECIALISTS IN COLONIAL AND FOREIGN WORK. ESTIMATES AND DESIGNS FREE ON APPLICATION.

FACSIMILE OF ROYAL WARRANT.

DESIGNERS AND MANUFACTURERS OF THE MOST LUXURIOUSLY APPOINTED MOTOR CARS. ANY TYPE OF CHASSIS SUPPLIED ON ADVANTAGEOUS TERMS. MOTOR BODIES DESIGNED TO SUIT INDIVIDUAL TASTE.

CARRIAGE AND MOTOR CAR BUILDERS TO THE NOBILITY AND GENTRY
OF GREAT BRITAIN,
HIS HIGHNESS THE RAJAH OF JOWAR,
AND MANY OTHER NATIVE GENTLEMEN OF INDIA.

WE HAVE OVER A CENTURY OF EXPERIENCE IN THE BEST CLASS OF CARRIAGE BUILDING. EVERY PART OF THE COMPLETED CARRIAGE IS MADE IN OUR OWN FACTORY FROM THE BEST MATERIALS BY EXPERIENCED WORKMEN, UNDER STRICT PERSONAL SUPERVISION. WE ARE GIVING THE SAME CARE AND ATTENTION TO OUR **MOTOR BODIES,** WHICH ARE BUILT OF CAREFULLY SELECTED MATERIALS, AND ARE FINISHED IN THE MOST PERFECT FASHION. REPAIRS OF EVERY DESCRIPTION—A SPECIALITY.

COMPETENT MEN SENT TO ANY PART OF THE COUNTRY TO TAKE INSTRUCTIONS. CARRIAGES AND MOTORS STORED AT MODERATE TERMS, IN SPECIALLY BUILT PREMISES.

AWARDED SILVER MEDALS CRYSTAL PALACE EXHIBITIONS, 1851 AND 1862.

A LARGE STOCK OF NEW AND SECOND-HAND CARRIAGES OF ALL KINDS ALWAYS ON VIEW AT OUR SHOWROOMS. CARRIAGES CAREFULLY PACKED AND SENT TO ANY PART OF THE WORLD.

Figure 1 Trade poster c. 1910.   (JSK)

Figure 2
Trade
card
c.1870.
(JSK)

The Flying Standard

BRITAIN'S WONDERFUL NEW CAR

Seats six in comfort within the wheelbase. Brilliant
Performance. Economical to run. 70 to 80 m.p.h.
according to model. Most luxurious equipment.
D.W.S. Permanent Jacking System. Two-compart-
ment locker in tail.

Telescopic Steering Column. Low running cost.
Britain's most beautiful and roomiest car at the price.

FLYING STANDARD 12 H.P. 4-CYL., **£259**
16 H.P. 6-CYL., **£299**
20 H.P. 6-CYL., **£315**

COME FOR A THRILLING TRIAL RUN TO—

WM. KINROSS & SONS
Established 1802.　　Appointed Makers to the Queen 1838.

PORT STREET : *Standard Agents* : **STIRLING**

Phone 309.　Models made by J. Ivester Lloyd, of Linedale, Leighton Buzzard.　Grams, 'Kinross'

Figure 3
Advert
1930's
(RMcC).

Figure 4 Section of carriage showroom. (Mackay)

From the mid 18th Century, Stirling became one of the principal centres of Coach Building in Great Britain. In 1865 the Bastion housed a forge as part of Kinross's famous Carriage Works. The first two-seated gig in Scotland was made by William Kinross and Sons. Appointed Carriage Builders to Her Majesty Queen Victoria. Horse Carriage trade developed to Motor-Driven Vehicles and by 1910 "the most luxuriously appointed motor cars" were sold at the new showroom building on Port Street.

Figure 5 Part of wall plaque in the Bastion monument, Thistle Centre. (LC)

Figure 6 Motor and carriage works, Port Street, 1923.

Figure 8 Delivery float, Reid Glen Farm Dairy.

Figure 7 Kinross building,
Port Street, now Marks & Spencer.

Figure 9
George Kinross, Provost 1891-97

Figure 10 John Kinross –
portrait by Alan Sutherland, 1968.

Figure 11 John Kinross building, University of Stirling.   (LC)

Figure 12 Stained glass window, Allan Park South Church.   L.C.

THE BICENTENARY OF THE RAPLOCH,
STIRLING'S GEORGIAN PLANNED VILLAGE

G. A. Dixon

Georgian Stirling was slow to join the Age of Improvement. First reached by a turnpike road in the 1750's (1), the Rock-borne backwater took fully 40 years to begin to sprout a network of new streets and settlement extensions such as was triggered by news of the approaching southern turnpike in Aberdeen, for example, in the 1790's (2). The Barras Yett (Burgh Gate) across Port Street was demolished in the 1770's "for Beautifying, Widening & Streigting the entry to the Burgh" (3), and four large building plots on the Bisset lands, each of several acres, from Viewforth to Annfield as later labelled, were feued off to middle-class citizens in 1785 in order to improve the southern approach to Stirling (4). The first planned urbanization of the relatively level fields encompassing the long-settled ridge of the Castle Rock to be successfully implemented, however, was the neat rectangle of building lots lying north of the Raploch Burn and east of the Craigforth-serving road from the Top of the Town to the bridge which had replaced the Drip Ferry over the Forth nearly 30 years previously (5).

"The haill Lands of Raplochs" had been bought for Cowane's Hospital "In name of the poor of the said hospitall" from Charles, Earl of Mar, in 1677, for £22,500 Scots (6), had seen a little group of fishermen's cottages, "Fisher Row", constructed due north of the Castle in 1696 (7), and had been let in a multiplicity of small arable lots to a diminishing number of agricultural tenants as the 18th century progressed (8). That the various remaining Raploch leases were all due to expire at the Martinmas term in 1798 (9) permitted the Town Council as Cowane's Patrons to reorganize the land between the Castle Rock and the Forth into essentially a single farm and, at its south-western corner, a tiny, and very basic, artisans' village. As the latter's foundation date approached, a mere handful of buildings stood around its site. Immediately south of the bridge carrying the high road across the Raploch Burn stood a twinned pair of Raplochburn cottages facing one another across the road just before it turned uphill towards Ballengeich; on an eighth of a Scots acre abutting the north-east corner of the bridge stood a single hut, and on the west side of the high road, now Raploch Road, some half way towards what came to be the Kildean junction once the Drip Road turnpike was constructed in 1812, stood a smithy (10). The road link running southwards from the Raploch to the Dumbarton Road turnpike constructed in the mid-1790's was not made until 1816 (11).

On 13th February 1798 the Cowane's Patrons, having agreed to provide new farm buildings that summer for the new single tenant of the Raploch Farm, James Christie, and having resolved to contribute £25 "towards supporting the nation against the threatened invasion of the French", turned to agreeing "to Few part: of the lands of Raploch fronting the road to

Craigforth, and remit to the Office Bearers or any three of them to adjust a plan for that purpose, and to fix the articles and conditions, And appoint the same to be sold by public roup within the Town house upon Saturday the third day of March next at eleven o'clock forenoon, and due advertisement of the roup to be made thro' the Town in the usual manner" (12).

In the event, it was not feus but notably long building leases which were granted to the first settlers in the new village. Such leases cost less than feu charters and in practice the 999 years' durations on offer must have seemed acceptably close to perpetuity; none, indeed, now remains in force only two centuries later.

The initial leasing plan of Raploch Village was drawn up by a local land surveyor, Robert Sconce (13), and comprised ten plots, no. 1, of "thirty two falls and fourteen elns Scots measure" at the south end of the single-sided street, with its southern boundary along the Raploch Burn, being let to the Raploch blacksmith, James Henderson. No. 2, just to the north, was taken by the Town Council "for building a house for their Customer" (14); no.3 was let to George Christie, a wright (i.e., joiner); no. 4 to Duncan Wright, a shoemaker; no. 5 to John Dougal, a weaver; no. 6 to Alexander Comrie, another weaver; no. 7 to Peter Strang, a tailor "lately in Moss of Blairdrummond", and no. 8 to Archibald Ferguson, a shoemaker (15). Lots 2 to 8 were all of 24 falls and between 10 and 33 square ells, or approximately a fifth of an imperial acre, in extent. The entry date on all eight of those early leases was the Martinmas term in November 1798; the leases themselves were signed by the relevant parties on various dates from 23rd May 1799 to 10th August 1799. The leases of lots 9 and 10, both of just under 24 falls in size and both to run for 997 years from Martinmas 1800, were signed by the lessees, "John McEwen weaver in Moss of Blair drummond" and "Duncan Campbell weaver in Glasgow" respectively, in February 1801 (16).

Some slow demand for Raploch building lots continuing, a second leasing plan, simply extending Sconce's rectangle northwards along Raploch Road and with similar lot sizes, was drawn up by William Drummond, land surveyor, nurseryman, and father of the pervasively powerful Drummond brothers of Victorian Stirling (17). Lots 1 and 2 on this new plan, for 999 years from Martinmas 1803, were let in February 1805 to James Christie, a wright; lot 3, in the same month, from the same term and with the same duration, was let to "William MacNab sometime Weaver in Dunblane" (18); lots 4 and 5 were let on the same basis to John McLaren, shoemaker, and David Stalker, described simply as a "residenter", respectively (19), and lots 6 and 7 to "John Cameron sometime servant to the Duke of Argyle at Roseneath", for 999 years from Martinmas 1804 (20). The annual rent for the building plots on both plans was set at just under a shilling a fall and the settlers were given two years "to build thereon and completely finish a dwelling house, work shop and offices" (i.e., sheds), each house's front wall not to "come within twenty feet" of the fence along Raploch Road, and this front strip to be "kept clear and unencumbered for the sake of embelishment". Settlers were also required to "have their middensteads behind their houses" and to "unyoke and lay up their empty carts and other utensils for agriculture or for trades behind their houses" (15, 17).

At that point, in August 1805, further leasing of building plots in direct continuation of the Sconce and Drummond plans ceased for several decades, though with effect from 1820 "George Ronald Spirit dealer at Raploch and Ann Thomson his Spouse" took a building lot of just over a quarter of an acre next to the new Kildean Toll-house at the north end of Raploch Road and Duncan Key and Alexander Meiklejohn took neighbouring, smaller lots there in 1829 (21). Across the southern edge of the gap ran the Forth and Clyde Junction railway from Stirling to Balloch, opened on 26th May 1856 (22).

In the meantime, however, the housing capacity on the existing Sconce-Drummond building lots had expanded quite substantially. Already by 1813 that symbol of a new village community, its own schoolmaster, had come upon the Raploch scene, with the appointment, from May of that year, of Samuel Forrester, at an annual salary from the Cowane's Patrons of three guineas (23). By the date of the first detailed census, that of 1841, 317 people, almost wholly Scottish in background, were recorded as residents. Among the 24 occupations and 125 individuals specified as so occupied, 45 weavers, with a further 23 inhabitants engaged in assorted textile and clothing trades, easily topped the table; 22 labourers, including 11 in agriculture, followed. Only 8 were named as being employed in the building trades. A hawker, a stone breaker, a spirit dealer and a surveyor figured among the singletons at the foot of the table. Among those not listed as employed were 9 of independent means and 3 army or navy pensioners.

Perhaps the most striking difference between the 1841 and the 1851 census returns for the Raploch was the nearly tenfold increase in the Irish-born element in the population. Of the 317 inhabitants in 1841, only 9 (fewer than 3 %) were recorded as having been born in Ireland. In 1851, 85, 23 % of the 374 total, were Irish-born. Had it not been for this post-potato-famine influx of Irish into the Raploch, its population would have shown a decline over the decade.

Structurally, planned-village Raploch survived into the middle decades of the present century. From the late 1920's onwards, local-authority housing spread across the fields around the Georgian village (24). Then the early 1950's, which clear-felled so much of the Top of the Town, also swept Revolutionary-era Raploch into the dustbin of history and the compulsory-purchase-order-aided tide of council houses flowed across its site as though it had never been (25).

Acknowledgements

The author is grateful to Stirling Council Archives Services for access to most of the sources listed below, and to Dr John Brims, Council Archivist, for permission to quote from them. Generous thanks are due to Bob McCutcheon for the rare Grassom 1817 map and plates of Raploch Village.

References/Sources

1. The Linlithgow Bridge to Stirling turnpike (25 Geo. II, c. 28); Stirling Town Council Minutes, B66/21/10, pp. 81, 188, 231.
2. Aberdeen Town Council Minutes, 1793 - 1800 : 1/l.LXVII, fo. 1.
3. B66/21/12, 4th August 1770, 4th November 1775.
4. B66/21/13, 22nd January 1785; SB1/10/16, pp. 91-122.
5. SB8/l/1, 6th May 1769; the roots of the Terraces lie in the decision of the Town Council as Spittal's Hospital Patrons on 5th October 1799 "to concert a plan for fewing part of the Hospitals ground in the laigh parks for houses and gardens in the forms of streets" : SB6/1/1; the feuing plan for Cowane Street is dated 1802 : MP/SB/47.
6. B66/20/5, 5th November 1677.
7. Harrison, J. G. : Fisher Row Planned Housing and the Declining Fishing Industry in late Seventeenth Century Stirling, *Forth Naturalist and Historian*, vol. 9 (1984-85), 1987, pp. 113-124. (out of print)
8. MP/SB/35 : McDougall's "Map of the Raplochs", 1759; SB5/4/1 : crop 1797 rental.
9. SB5/4/1 : crop 1798 rental.
10. MP/SB/35 : A Plan of the Raploch lands, : [Robert Sconce], c. 1790.
11. SB6/1/1, 11th October 1794, 24th October 1796; B66/21/15 : 18th November 1815 and 16th November 1816.
12. SB5/l/5, 13th February 1798.
13. SB1/11/1/215/1; neither original feuing/leasing plan survives.
14. I.e., collector of local taxes there, as at the other entrances to the town: B66/23/8, 1798-99 accounts, p. 17.
15. The eight original leases survive as SB1/11/1/215/1-8.
16. B66/9/20, p. 320.
17. SB6/6/43/1-3; Industries of Stirling and District, Stirling Council Library Services, 1998, pp. 84-91.
18. SB6/6/43/1-2.
19. SB6/6/43/2-3, where they are recorded as contiguous lessees.
20. SB6/6/1/43/3.
21. B1/11/1/240; SB5/4/1.
22. *Stirling Observer*, 29th May 1856, p. 3.
23. SB5/l/5, under date 6th April 1813; SB5/3/8, p. 122.
24. SB1/1/37, p. 320; SB1/1/38, p. 39.
25. SBl/1/60, pp. 16-17.

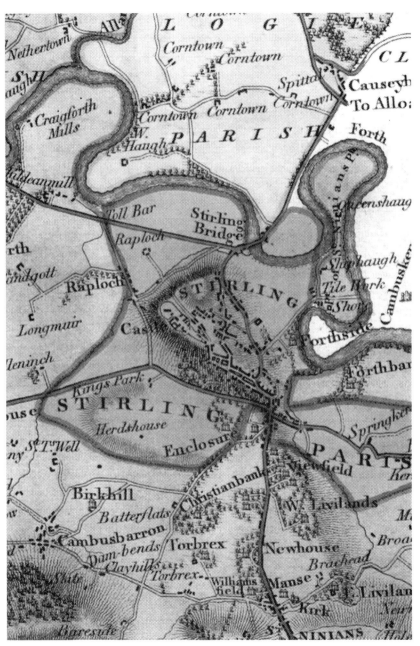

Stirling area of Grassom's 1817 map of Stirlingshire.
(R. McCutcheon)

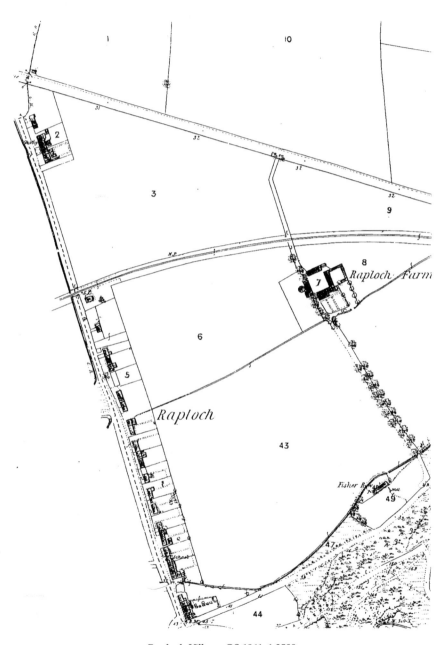

Raploch Village OS 1861 1:2500.

View of Raploch Village, Stirling Castle on the left, c1900.

(R. McCutcheon)

Raploch Village and the Plain of Menteith from Stirling Castle, c1900.

(R. McCutcheon)

BOOK REVIEW (Historical)

The Bruce. John Barbour (c.1375) an edition with translation and notes by A. A. M. Duncan. 1997. Canongate Classics. 800pp. ISBN 0-86241-681-7. £9.99.

Here is one of the masterpieces of Scottish literature. This Archdeacon of Aberdeen's epic poem is presented afresh, translated in a readable style, with parallel learned and illuminating notes by Professor Duncan. This noted Scottish academic historian speaks from a life-long special interest in King Robert the Bruce, and in this classic work of Barbour's. Alive with dramatic descriptions of travels by land and sea, escapes, combats, sieges, battles, the blood spattered reality of chivalry, it is above all an invocation of freedom for our land which resonates powerfully in this late 20th century.

This welcome work is a much appreciated and desirable reassessment and clarification of the history of the Bruce as recounted dramatically in verse by the poet Barbour. This poem has been a key source for studies of the life of Robert Bruce by writers great and small, popular and academic over many years; from Bowen's voluminous Scotichronicon of the 1440s to the present day. It includes much information not found anywhere else.

The contents page of this bulky paperback is a helpful chart – from Duncan's 38 page introduction surveying the background, sources, history; through the presentation of the 20 books of *The Bruce*, page by opposing page with commentaries, interpretations, notes to p.773. Then appendices, including the *Declaration of Arbroath* – the letter of the Scottish magnates to Pope John XXII of April 1320; and a special 10 page index.

As Duncan says – "I hope you buy this book to read as one of the masterpieces of Scottish literature."

L.C.

THE BUILT AND ARCHAEOLOGICAL HERITAGE OF THE FORTH

P. J. Ashmore, Historic Scotland and I. Oxley, Maritime Fife

Introduction

At the coastline of the Firth of Forth many interests converge which involve the cultural heritage. There are human pressures on it, such as commercial and industrial developments, aggregate dredging, fishing, defence works, pollution, and treasure hunting. Natural processes such as erosion, subsidence, sedimentation and sea level rise can damage sites and buildings. Recreation and tourism both depend in part upon and affect the cultural heritage, as does our sense of belonging. They are important to our understanding of what underlies Scotland's sense of identity.

In recent years, in order to understand this complexity, various coastal assessment surveys have been sponsored by Historic Scotland. They have been carried out from Dunbar to Stirling on the south shore, and from Stirling to the border of Fife on the north shore by Glasgow University Archaeological Research Division (GUARD 1996); and within Fife by Maritime Fife (Robertson 1996). This work has shown that some 800 known archaeological sites lie within a coastal strip 50 m wide in the Lothians, Falkirk, Stirling, Clackmannan, and

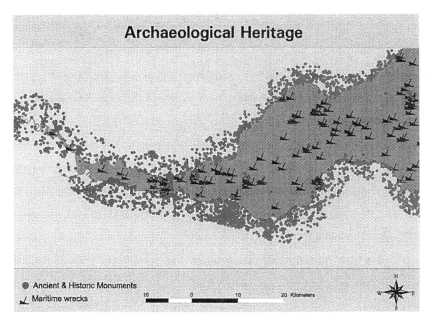

Figure 1 Archaeological heritage of Forth – map.

(FEF)

100 m wide on the Fife coast (Figure 1). Some 70 of these have been scheduled for protection under the Ancient Monuments and Archaeological Areas Act 1979. In addition, fossil landscapes of considerable antiquity and importance survive buried by later sediments both inland and on the sea floor. There are more than 500 listed buildings (listed as worthy of protection under the Planning (Listed Buildings and Conservation Areas) (Scotland) Act 1997) within 50 m of the coast and many other structures important to the rich maritime and defensive history of the Firth of Forth. It has over 150 wrecks recorded in the National Monuments record (dating mainly to the last 200 years) but it is likely to contain many more sites, and much earlier sites if recent work in comparable estuaries such as the Thames and the Severn is any guide.

A little prehistory and history

The complex shoreline history of the Firth of Forth, following melting of the glaciers, is partially preserved in raised beaches, and in sediments and buried land surfaces. Hunter-gatherer sites under marine deposits at the head of the Forth Estuary, including finds of whale skeletons and antler tools, are potentially of international significance. One of the two earliest hunter gatherer settlements in Scotland, dating in round terms to 7500 BC, has recently been found near Fife Ness. Hunter-gatherers and (from about 4000 BC) farmers left mounds of marine shells, and flint tools, on raised beaches, sites commonly referred to as 'middens'.

There is a curious lack of information firmly dated to the period from 4000 to 3000 BC, apart from exciting recent discoveries at Chapelfield, Cowie (Figure 2), which reaffirm the potential of sites not normally visible. Flat middens on the Lothian coast contain finds of kinds commonly associated with major ceremonial sites and settlements of the period from 3000 to 2500 BC.

There is abundant evidence for burials in the period from 2500 to 750 BC, and abundant artefacts imply as yet unlocated coastal settlement. Judging by other parts of Scotland there will have been increasing agricultural exploitation of all available land towards the end of this period, including sandy coastal strips.

Native forts and burials from the period between 750 BC and AD 650 are found all along the south coast. It seems highly likely that close examination of the coast edge will reveal evidence of field systems and even settlements. There are many cropmark settlements of the pre-Roman part of this period. Remains left by the Romans include the Antonine Wall (Figure 3), with the Roman fort and settlement at Carriden and several temporary camps. No Roman harbour structures have yet been revealed (although there should be remains of Roman ports at Cramond and Inveresk, and presumably a Roman bridging, fording or ferry point somewhere near Stirling).

In addition to (probable) use or reuse of native forts in the post-Roman period, several settlement and burial sites are known. There were Anglian coastal settlements along the south coast near the sea. In addition there are many cemeteries with burials in long cists near the coasts of Lothian and Fife. It is very likely that other important coastal remains of the Picts, Britons, Angles, Scots and the Norse between AD 650 and AD 1000 survive, as yet unlocated.

From about AD 1000 to the Reformation the shores of the Forth reflect both the hierarchical lay society and the powerful church of the Medieval Kingdom. Many castles and tower houses survive, some of exceptional merit (e.g. Alloa Figure 4), with a few sites of medieval villages. In addition there are many chapels, churches and, on the north side, unusually many monastic establishments (e.g. Cambuskenneth Abbey Figure 5). The late medieval parish churches of coastal Fife are exceptionally rich and complex. Most of the coastal burghs, centring around harbours, had their origin in the period, towards the end of which coastal artillery fortifications were built. From after the Reformation there are interesting succession of parish churches in many coastal towns. Cromwellian forts were built. The cores of the burghs expanded into small towns.

The industrial revolution happened early in Falkirk (e.g. Carron Ironworks), Fife and Lothian, and its remains are beginning to be recognised as of considerable importance. The Forth boasts a rich industrial heritage including, notably, salt works, coal mining, potteries, grain mills, agriculture, naval installations, harbours (e.g. Alloa Figure 6), lighthouses, gasworks, power stations, transport and bridges. Many such sites would have been cleared as derelict a few decades ago, but are now beginning to be recognised as of great importance to our understanding of Scotland. Great houses were built or created from smaller dwellings. Holiday resorts became common and ports and towns expanded. Regency, Victorian and recent remains include the Martello tower at Leith and twentieth century batteries, together with pill boxes, glider traps and many other martial relics. A wave of innovative post-war social housing redevelopment considerably altered the cores of many old Fife burghs.

Current work

Much work is being undertaken to record this rich heritage. The Royal Commission on the Ancient and Historical Monuments of Scotland (RCAHMS) has recently extended the remit of the National Monuments Record of Scotland out to the 12 miles territorial waters limit – approaching 200 sites have been recorded. The majority are late nineteenth and twentieth century wrecks. New research into the post-war redevelopments of the coastal burghs of Fife and the Lothians is being undertaken. Burgh Surveys sponsored by Historic Scotland include new surveys of coastal burghs and updates of old ones in the Forth area; and an education pack has been created. The Defence of Britain project aims to record all late 19th century and later fortifications. It is under the aegis of the Council for British Archaeology and is administered in the Forth Estuary by the Council for Scottish Archaeology. *The Survey of 20th Century Defences* for the old Fife Region (1996) and Lothian Region (1997), prepared by John Guy for Historic Scotland, is being used by volunteers to enhance the record. Copies are available in major local libraries. A survey for the 'Central Region' area should be completed in 1998. RCAHMS is developing the air photographic resource with a particular emphasis on the islands of the Forth.

Maritime Fife, a project team based in the Scottish Institute of Maritime Studies of St Andrews University, aims to survey, record and research the maritime historical and archaeological resource preserved in the coastal, foreshore and seabed areas of Fife (Oxley nd). It has received funding from Fife Council and from Historic Scotland. The project combines academic research with fieldwork (ranging from shore walks to evaluations of underwater sites) which involve members of the public, local and national organisations. Maritime Fife is also involved in focal studies of important coastal sites in Fife, including the north banks of the Forth, sponsored by Historic Scotland through Fife Council. These have been incorporated in the Fife Shoreline Management Plan recently commissioned by Fife Council.

Historic Scotland is carrying out a national resurvey of Listed Buildings. In the Forth area it has recently been active in Granton, Pilton, Dalmeny and Kirkcaldy. It is also assessing the threat to the coastal cultural heritage from marine erosion.

Coastal Assessment Surveys form an important part of an initiative to characterise the coastal archaeological and historic buildings resource by itemising archaeological sites and areas, historic buildings, and the geomorphology and erosion status of the areas in which they lie. Glasgow University Archaeological Research Division (GUARD) was sponsored to produce a survey of the Lothian, Falkirk, Stirling and Clackmannan shores of the Forth and Maritime Fife was sponsored by Historic Scotland to produce a report for the coastline from the boundary of Fife Region in the west to Fifeness.

The surveys have shown that evidence for a rich archaeological resource survives in the coastal and intertidal areas of the Forth. The discovery of such remains as middens at Alloa, Anstruther, Crail and Elie; early burials at Lundin Links and the Wemyss Caves under threat from coastal erosion; shoreline hulks at Alloa, North Queensferry and Kincardine (Wood 1997a and Figure 7); a possible inter-tidal stone structure at Crombie (Wood 1997b); and early post-medieval coastal defences on the margins of designed landscapes such as that at Dalmeny are but an indication of the full archaeological potential of this area.

New ideas

Discussions are taking place on a further initiative, Shorewatch, to provide a structure within which local community based groups can monitor the affects of erosion on the cultural heritage. Fife Council and Maritime Fife are involved in heritage aspects of Fife Coast Watch while the Council for Scottish Archaeology, sponsored by Historic Scotland, is assessing Health and Safety issues with a view to the involvement of Young Archaeologist Clubs and other community-oriented groups.

What next?

The main issues are the need to ensure that the cultural heritage is considered in all decision making processes, that the inventory of the cultural heritage resource, both above and below the shoreline, is adequate; and that the value and importance of the cultural heritage are promulgated. Judgements on what should be preserved in the face of threats from natural forces and development, and on what should be promoted for peoples education and enjoyment, should be soundly based on generally accepted criteria.

Timely consideration of the cultural heritage is important. If the cultural heritage is dealt with fully in strategic and local development control plans, and if its value and vulnerability is taken into account in proposals for individual developments, costly or inadequate mitigation measures can be avoided. In schemes to protect the coast, the early consideration of the implications for the natural heritage and for downstream areas should be matched by those for the cultural heritage.

Crucial to this is a proper information base. Archaeological sites are constantly being discovered and despite rapid recent progress the inventory of dry land, intertidal and submerged sites is incomplete. In addition to targeted surveys, there is a requirement for a better understanding of the various environments of the Forth in which sites can be expected to survive – particularly of the nature, condition, extent, vulnerability and importance of completely submerged sites.

Why we should care

The value and importance of the cultural heritage are considerable. Although it is usually hard to assess the contributions of individual heritage sites and buildings, the cultural heritage provides a major economic benefit through its contribution to quality of life and through the attraction of tourists. In addition it helps to give the region its unique character and contains much hidden evidence for its history. The cultural heritage is a non-renewable resource because, although the form of an archaeological or historical site can be partially recreated, scientific and historical information within its layers cannot. Continued preservation most often depends upon objects, structures and deposits remaining buried and undisturbed. Underwater, in the right physical and chemical conditions, the range and quality of preservation of any organic materials can be far better than that on most land sites. However, these sites can be correspondingly sensitive to disturbance.

Threats and opportunities

The built heritage is an irreplaceable resource which helps give Scotland its unique character. Its preservation and sympathetic, sustainable exploitation will help to ensure that the Forth has a sound economic and cultural future. There is a constant need to make informed judgements about what should be preserved. Provided that important sites and buildings have been recognised through survey, possible responses to proposed change and to natural threats include preservation, recording of various intensities, and doing nothing.

There are plentiful opportunities to continue promotion of the Forth area through its heritage in a sustainable way. The Forth has a rich maritime history which may be found in academic institutions, local archives and in the memories of local people whose experiences involved the sea in any form. Documentary sources include Admiralty Court Records, Burgh Records, private muniments and early cartographic records. There is also great value to be found in maritime-related collections in national and local museums.

There are already successful key entry points to the area, and there are many intermediate sized sites and many smaller scale sites to provide foci for initiatives such as visitor centres or locations for film, television and other media (e.g. the historic docks of Alloa and Bo'ness, and Forthside in Stirling). The emphasis of Local Agenda 21 Plans on community involvement and wise use of non-renewable resources can be translated directly into plans for use of the heritage for economic development.

Heritage provides an exceptionally effective tool for teaching about Scotland's complex history and the background to its current success. There is a growing awareness of the extent to which it can enrich the curriculum and an increasing number of teaching packs which emphasise the fieldwork and site-oriented aspects of exploring the built heritage of the Forth.

The highest priorities are –

- to increase awareness, particularly amongst decision makers, of the importance and value of the cultural heritage;

- to improve information about all sites, monuments and buildings of architectural or historic interest;

- to improve enjoyment of all sites, monuments and buildings of architectural or historic interest;

- to improve accessibility to all sites, monuments and buildings of architectural or historic interest;

- to improve standards and methodologies for recording sites in advance of threats;

- to develop responses to marine erosion and damage to the built and archaeological heritage.

Acknowledgements

This paper is based on one produced by the Forth Estuary Forum's Archaeology and Built Heritage Topic Group, including from time to time the authors, David Easton, Sarah Govan, Nick Haynes, Lorna Main, Paula Martin, Geoff Moy, Diana Murray, Robert Prescott and Peter Yeoman and with input also from, amongst others, Mark Jennison, Deanna Groom, the National Monuments Record for Scotland and Dan Hillier.

References and further reading:

Anson, P. F., 1930, Fishing Boats and Fisherfolk on the East Coast of Scotland. London.

Armit, Ian, 1997, Celtic Scotland. Batsford & Historic Scotland.

Ashmore, P. J., 1996, Neolithic and Bronze Age Scotland. Batsford & Historic Scotland.

Ashmore, P. J., 1993, Archaeology and the Coastal Zone: Towards an Historic Scotland Policy. Edinburgh.

Baird, B., 1993, Shipwrecks of the Forth. Nekton Books, Glasgow.

Breeze, D. J., 1996, Roman Scotland. Batsford & Historic Scotland.

Browne, M. A. E., 1987, The physical geography and geology of the estuary and Firth of Forth, Scotland. *Proceedings of the Royal Society, Edinburgh 93B*, 235-244.

Browne, M. A. E., Meldrum, J. R. and Munro, S. K. 1993, Geology pp1-17. *In* Central Scotland – land, wildlife, people. Forth Naturalist and Historian.

Campbell, R. H., 1961, The Carron Company. Edinburgh.

Campbell, R. H., 1997, Scotland since 1707, the rise of an industrial society. John Donald.

Clackmannanshire Field Studies Society. 1997. Alloa Tower and the Erskines of Mar. 3rd edition.

Collard, M., 1998, The Cramond Lioness. *Scottish Archaeological News*, 27: 8-9.

Cunningham-Dobson, N., 1997a, Shipwreck Heritage of Fife. Maritime Fife, University of St Andrews. Unpublished report.

Ditchburn, D., 1993, Piracy and War at Sea in late Medieval Scotland. *In* Smout, T. C., *Scotland and the Sea*. John Donald.

Fife Regional Council, 1989, Fife's Early Archaeological Heritage – A Guide.

Foster, S., 1996, Picts, Gaels and Scots. Batsford & Historic Scotland.

Gifford, J., 1988, The Buildings of Scotland: Fife.

Gifford, J., McWilliam, C., & Walker, D., 1984, The Buildings of Scotland: Edinburgh.

Graham, A., 1968, Archaeological notes on some harbours in Eastern Scotland. *Proceedings of the Society of Antiquaries of Scotland*, 101: 200-285.

GUARD, 1996, Coastal Assessment Survey: the Firth of Forth from Dunbar to the Border of Fife. Historic Scotland.

Harding-Hill, R., 1993, The Moray Firth Review. Scottish Natural Heritage, Inverness.

Hartley, J. P. & Clark R. N., (eds.), 1987, Environmental effects of North Sea oil and gas developments. *Philosophical Transactions of the Royal Society of London B316*, 459-67.

Hendrie, W. F., 1996, Discovering the River Forth. John Donald.

Hendrie, W. F., 1998, Discovering the Firth of Forth. John Donald.

Historic Scotland Education Unit 1998 Investigating Scotland's Burghs.

Hume, J. R., 1977, The Industrial Archaeology of Scotland Volume 1: The Lowlands and Borders. Batsford.

Jacques, R. & McKean, C., 1994, RIAS Illustrated Guide: West Lothian.

Lambeck, K., 1995. Late Devensian and Holocene shorelines of the British Isles and North Sea from models of glacio-hydro-isostatic rebound. *Journal of the Geological Society 152*, 437-448.

Land Use Consultants, 1987, An Inventory of Designed Landscapes in Scotland.

Mackie, E. W., 1972, Radiocarbon dates for two Mesolithic shell heaps and a Neolithic axe factory in Scotland. *Proceedings of the Prehistorical Society* 38, 412-416.

Martin, C. J. M., 1993, Water Transport and the Roman Occupation in North Britain. *In* Smout, T. C., Scotland and the Sea. John Donald.

McKean, C., 1985, RIAS Illustrated Guide: Stirling & the Trossachs.

McKean, C., 1992, RIAS Illustrated Guide: Edinburgh.

McWilliam, C., 1978, Buildings of Scotland: Lothian.

Mowat, S., 1994, The Port of Leith: Its history and its people. John Donald.

Oxley, I., nd, Maritime Fife: An integrated study of the maritime archaeological and historical resource of Fife. In *Proceedings of the Institute of Landscape Studies and Nautical Archaeology Society* conference 'Archaeology in Coastal Landscapes', 29th-31st March, 1996, Portsmouth University. (In press).

Oxley, I., 1998, Archaeological Shoreline Management Plans: Focal Studies for Historic Scotland. Scottish Institute of Maritime Studies, University of St Andrews. Unpublished report.

Pride, G., 1990, The Kingdom of Fife: an illustrated architectural guide. Edinburgh.

RCAHMS, 1929, Inventory: Midlothian & West Lothian.

RCAHMS, 1933, Inventory: Fife, Kinross & Clackmannan.

RCAHMS, 1951, Inventory: Edinburgh.

Ridley, G., 1985, Dive Scotland Volume III – The Northern Isles and East Coast. London.

Ritchie, A., 1994, Viking Scotland. Batsford & Historic Scotland.

Robertson, P., 1996, Coastal Assessment Survey for Historic Scotland: Kincardine to Fife Ness. Maritime Fife, University of St Andrews. Unpublished report.

Sissons, J. B., 1976a, The geomorphology of the upper Forth Valley. *Forth Naturalist and Historian 1*, 5-20

Sissons, J. B., 1976b, The geomorphology of the British Isles: Scotland. Methuen.

Sloan, D., 1993, Sample Site and System: Shell Midden Economies in Scotland 6000 to 4000 BP. Dissertation for the degree of Doctor of Philosophy Cambridge.

SOED, 1994, National Planning Policy Guideline NPPG 42 Archaeology and Planning. Scottish Office Environment Department.

SOED, 1994, Planning Advice Note PAN 42 Archaeology – the Planning process and Scheduled Monuments Procedures.

The First, Second and Third Statistical Accounts for Clackmannan, for East Lothian, for Fife, for Midlothian, for Stirlingshire and West Lothian. Steer, J. A., 1973, The Coastline of Scotland. Cambridge.

Swan, A., 1987, RIAS Illustrated Guide: Clackmannan & the Ochils.

Tabraham, C. and Grove, D., 1995, Fortress Scotland and the Jacobites. Batsford & Historic Scotland.

Walker, B. & Ritchie, G., 1987, Exploring Scotland's Heritage; Fife & Tayside. RCAHMS.

Watters, B., 1998, Where Iron Runs Like Water: a new history of Carron Iron Works, 1759-1982. John Donald.

Wickham-Jones, C. R., 1994, Scotland's First Settlers. Batsford & Historic Scotland.

Wood, A. J. P. W., 1997a, Kincardine Foreshore Survey. Maritime Fife, University of St Andrews. Unpublished report.

Wood, A. J. P. W., 1997b, Crombie Point. Maritime Fife. Unpublished report.

Wood, A. J. P. W., 1997c, East Wemyss Gasworks. Maritime Fife. Unpublished report.

Yeoman, P., 1997, Medieval Scotland, Batsford & Historic Scotland.

(GUARD)

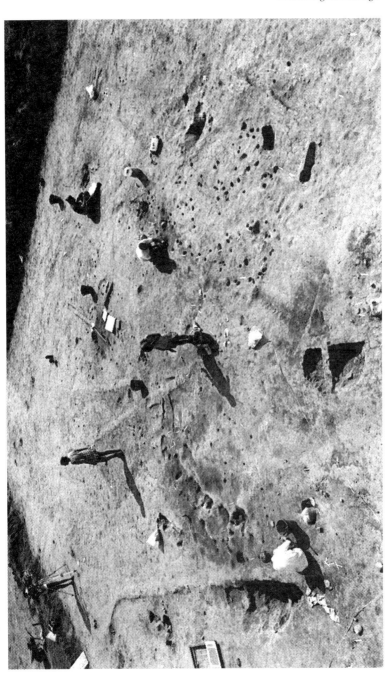

Figure 2 Neolithic House, Chapelfield, Cowie.

Figure 3 Antonine Wall, Forthlet – Kinneil House in background.

(L. Main and Falkirk Museum)

Figure 4 Alloa Tower.

(A. Conoboy)

Figure 5 Cambuskenneth Abbey, Bell Tower, foundations of cloister and nave.
(L. Main)

(L. Corbett)

Figure 6 Alloa Harbour.

(I. Oxley)

Figure 7 Marine archaeology at Kincardine.

AN EARLY STIRLING CHURCH

R. Page and C. Page

The earliest Ordnance Survey maps showed the 'Supposed site' of the Dominican Friary in Stirling situated in Murray Place behind the present Post Office as might be expected at the foot of Friars Street, previously Friars Wynd. This position, however, was entirely based on verbal tradition given to the Ordnance Survey team in 1858 (OSNB), unsupported by documentary evidence, and consequently was not included in later editions of OS maps.

Nevertheless when the foundations were being prepared in 1904 for the building which is now No 64 Murray Place, a massive stone wall with four substantial buttresses was discovered, and this was recognised by Bailie Ronald, Master of Works of the Town at that time, as being likely to be the south wall of the Blackfriars' Church (Ronald, 1904). Careful study of the documentary evidence in the Stirling archives enabled us to show that Bailie Ronald was correct, and that the wall he found was where the Blackfriars' Church must have been situated (Page and Page, 1996). We were grateful to obtain permission from the owners of 64 Murray Place to excavate in the garden behind the property to look for further traces of the Church. We were able to discover the outline of the Church from traces of the walls which still persisted, though they were far less substantial than the wall found in 1904 (Page and Page, 1996-7).

The Church as revealed by excavation was 27.5 m long with a chancel 13.5 m long and 6.5 m wide, with walls 1.5 m thick. It had a semicircular apse at the eastern end. Such apses had gone out of fashion before the Blackfriars, at the invitation of Alexander II, came to Stirling in 1233. It is therefore unlikely that they built their own church, probably they were given an existing church to use for their vocation of preaching to the lay population. It is known that this happened at York, although we have no documentary evidence in Scotland for a similar procedure.

When we came across a plan of St Margaret's Church in Dunfermline (RCAHMS, 1933) we realised that the design was very like the Stirling Blackfriars' Church, even the dimensions were very similar – see Figure 1.

St Margaret's Church lies under the Dunfermline Abbey Church. It was excavated in 1916, and its outline is traced by strips of bronze on the floor of the nave of the Abbey Church. The remains are preserved under the nave, and access is possible by arrangement with Historic Scotland. The western, more substantial part of the remains are believed to be a 10/11th century manorial or palace church. The eastern part, more flimsy, with an apse as at Stirling, was apparently the church of St. Margaret, circa 1072, as recorded by her confessor and biographer Turgot.

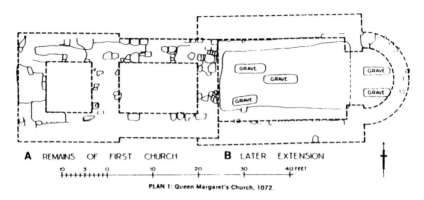

A REMAINS OF FIRST CHURCH   **B** LATER EXTENSION

PLAN 1: Queen Margaret's Church, 1072.

Figure 1 Ancient Churches:
Above, St Margaret's Church, under the nave of Dunfermline Abbey.
Below, Church of the Blackfriars, Stirling.
(Both to same scale.)

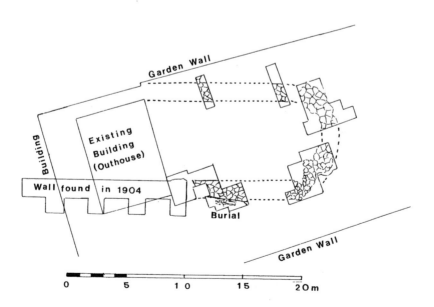

There seems good reason to think that the Stirling church which later came into the possession of the Blackfriars was contemporary with the Dunfermline church. The similarities, namely with two apparent phases of construction, with naves and chancels differing in solidity, and with closely corresponding dimensions, and both with semicircular apses, seem to indicate more than contemporaneity. A charter of King David (Lawrie 1905) gives to the abbey of Dunfermline "a *mansura* in Stirling with two churches and a ploughgate of land". A footnote in the inventory for Stirlingshire (RCAHMS 1963) referring to the Holy Rude Church says "By the middle of the 12th century the Abbey of Dunfermline was in possession of two churches in the 'vill' of Stirling, one of which was no doubt a predecessor of the present building."

It seems possible that the Church of the Blackfriars in Stirling, which was revealed by our excavation, was the other very early church possessed by Dunfermline Abbey, that the chancel with its semicircular apse was approximately of the date of Queen Margaret, and that the more substantial building which became the nave of the Blackfriars' Church was still earlier.

References

Lawrie, A. C. (1905). Early Scottish Charters. CCIX, Confirmation by King David of all the lands and rights of the Abbey of Dunfermline, c.1150.

OSNB (1858). Ordnance Survey Name Book 24, p74, quoted by National Monuments Records of Scotland, Edinburgh.

Page, R. and Page, C. (1996). Blackfriars of Stirling. *Proceedings of the Society of Antiquaries of Scotland* 126, 881-898.

Page, R. and Page, C. (1996-7). An Excavation at the Church of the Blackfriars, Stirling. *Glasgow Archaeological Journal* 20, 103-111.

RCAHMS (1933). Royal Commission on Ancient and Historical Monuments of Scotland, Inventory of Monuments in Fife. p105, No 197.

RCAHMS (1963). *Ibid.* Inventory of Monuments in Stirlingshire. vol 1, 129, No 131.

Ronald, J. (1904). On finding part of an old wall in Murray Place. *Transactions of the Stirling Natural History and Archaeological Society* 26, 126-130.

BOOK REVIEWS (Historical)

Where Iron Runs Like Water! Brian Watters. A new history of Carron Iron Works, 1759-1982. 1998. John Donald. 250pp. ISBN 0-85976-505-9. £10.95.

An early and major example of the Industrial Revolution; technological history was made at Carron by Watt, Boulton, Roebuck, and reputations for peacetime – elegant fireplaces, and for wartimes – armaments, notably the 'Cannonade'.

The author has had a life-long interest in the Carron Company – as an employee and as a local historian, fuelled by *The Story of Carron Company* in the bicentenary year 1959, and by Roy Campbell's *Carron Company* of 1961. His approach has been slightly different, driven by an interest in what the Works did in the district, the fascinating characters who frequent the story, the technical developments. The story is presented chronologically.

Using source material Watters recounts the early struggles for control of Roebuck and the founders, the formidable Charles Gascoigne, the century of Stainton/Dawson. Despite financial impropriety on a grand scale the Company was one of the great Victorian enterprises, with domestic manufacture in peace, and armaments in wars, it remained powerful even when tastes in new technology superceded the demand for iron products. The collapse of 1982 surprised the locality which had been shaped and changed by its iron making and other activities for over two centuries.

L.C.

The Bannockburn Years. William Scott. Luath Press. ISBN 0-946487-34-0. 232pp. £7.95.

In a way this volume should not be reviewed for the *Forth Naturalist and Historian* as it is an 'historical' novel. Its launch, however, last March included press releases that indicated that it "threw new light on the Battle of Bannockburn and advanced the best theory yet as to why Robert the Bruce and his army defeated a much larger force under Edward the Second".

The launch, however, explained why the author describes the battle in the way that he does. It is obvious from his description that he has no real knowledge of the topography of the Stirling area, then or now, and he certainly does not understand why this was the one spot where Bruce could possible make a stand.

Bruce had been waging a successful guerrilla type campaign and did not really want to engage in a fixed battle. At Bannockburn, however, he could take advantage of the unique landscape features – the low lying carse where the Bannock emerges from the dryfield, the steep sided gorge which runs from the carse to Milton, the narrow area where the burn can be forded there, the bogs at Milton and, at that period, the wooded areas on the edge of the New Park.

If things went wrong or, if Bruce decided not to fight, his army could retreat up the Bannock to the valley of the Carron and the Endrick to Sir John de Graeme's castle or retreat along the north of the Gargunnock hills to the Fords of Frew or beyond. He and his army could thus live to fight another day.

The topography lead to the events of the 23rd of June with Robert Clifford and a party of cavalry leaving the main advance body of the English army on Plean Muir and advancing via the edge of the carse towards Stirling Castle. Not in the attempt to relieve it but in order to start a circle movement to the rear of Bruce. This cavalry force was defeated on the level area outside the town, near to where the present police headquarters stand, by a body of foot soldiers under Thomas Randolph and was forced to retreat, demoralised and beaten, back towards the burn.

At the same time, the vanguard of the English force advanced towards the upstream of the Borestone. An area of trees and whin bushes, this was difficult ground for cavalry and was made more so by the use of disguised pits. Here was the single handed defeat of de Bohun by a lightly equipped Bruce. Another blow to the morale of the invading army.

These attempts to encircle Bruce's army having failed, Edward was left with two choices. He could attack through the area of the ford at Milton on a very narrow front or take his army down to the carse, cross the burn and come back up onto the dryfield. Perhaps remembering the effects of an army fighting on a narrow front at Stirling Bridge, Edward chose the latter.

Only part of the English army could get across and this would help to even out the opposing forces the next day. Edward's force never made it back up the dryfield to defeat the Scots but ended up being pushed over the gorge banks or onto the carse. For most of them it did not matter as they were to be killed or captured anyway.

After the main action on the 24th some of the English on the north bank escaped to Stirling Castle. Edward was included in this number but entry to the castle was denied by Mowbray the governor. Escape would have been nearly impossible if the main action had taken place on the carse where the Bannock meets the Forth.

Many of those on the south bank were also slaughtered, some already fleeing, while many did not realise the battle was over until fallen upon by the victorious Scots. Edward escaped by circling behind the Scots on the route that the English cavalry was meant to take the day before.

Instead of looking sensibly at topography, tactics and the course of the battle and its aftermath the author advances his own theory that the battle was fought entirely on the carse. He puts forward the claim that the Scots had a secret weapon in a host of long bowmen. He publicly stated at the launch that all historians are wrong and that there are no contemporary sources. He therefore picked a not very good current guide book based on a forty-year-old article and decorated with a twenty-year-old fantasy painting. He counted the multitude of tiny Scots figures on this totally imaginative cover and started from there. The result is a travesty of the truth that some of the excellent research by historians such as Professor Barrow has shown.

There are two good features of this 'historical' novel. One is the front cover by that gifted young artist Owain Kirby and the other is the list of some of the other publications by the go-ahead Luath Press at the end. Buy it and read it as entertainment with a local twist, but not as "new light on the Battle of Bannockburn".

Bob McCutcheon

PS At the launch the author expressed the wish that someone should excavate the mysterious hillock which intruded into his battle site on the carse and is not mentioned by any historian. Well I have mentioned it but it was in context with the history of coal mining in this area. It is the remains of the waste bing for Polmaise 1 and 2.

MENSTRIE GLEN: ARCHAEOLOGY, HISTORY AND LANDSCAPE –
forthcoming in 1999. RCAHMS.

A combined archaeological and historical survey of the Menstrie Glen, in the Ochils to the north-east of Stirling, will be published in 1999 by The Royal Commission on the Ancient and Historical Monuments of Scotland with the support of the Forth Naturalist and Historian, and Clackmannanshire Library Services. The survey traces the patterns of settlement and landuse from prehistory, but the nature of the surviving field remains and the historical sources emphasise the last 500 years.

The contraction of arable farming from the hills over the last two centuries or so has preserved an extensive and complex pre-improvement farming landscape, dotted with ruinous farmsteads. Rig cultivation swathes much of the lower ground, and field banks enclose both cultivated ground and grazing, demonstrating a complexity that hints at the dynamism and longevity of these farms. Shieling-huts in grazings on the higher ground and mining remains add further diversity to this landscape.

By happy coincidence the area has furnished a wealth of historical material that has been extensively researched by John Harrison. Not only does this provide a chronological framework for settlement over the last 500 years, but some sources also elucidate the processes that lie behind the archaeological remains. Particularly detailed records were kept by James Wright from the 1750s, outlining the improvement of his farm, from planting trees to rebuilding steadings. These records are especially valuable in that they span a period of considerable change in the Scottish rural landscape and highlight specific details of what was being planted in individual fields as well as general patterns, such as removal of tenants to create grazings.

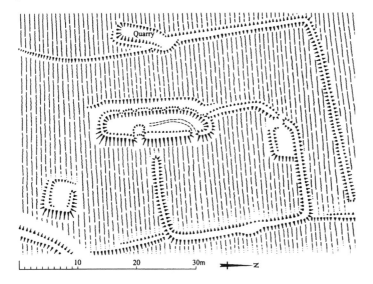

Figure 1

There is a growing recognition of the value of surviving pre-improvement landscapes in Scotland, and Menstrie Glen is a particularly fine example. The remarkably well-preserved field archaeology combined with the wealth of historical material will be a significant contribution to the history of the Scottish landscape.

The survey drawing (Figure 1) shows what survives of a farmstead of 18th century or earlier date. Indentations in the line of the decayed turf walls of the byre-house at the centre of the plan may mark the positions of the crucks that carried the roof. The building, which is terraced into a steep slope, was divided into a habitation and a byre, the latter with a drain along its centre. During the course of the 18th century farmsteads such as these were replaced by those with a more regular layout around a courtyard and a greater emphasis on stone for construction.

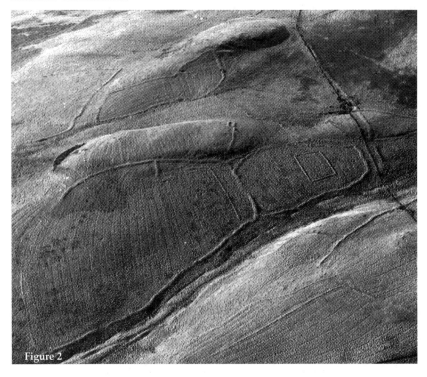

Figure 2

This oblique aerial photograph (Figure 2) above records a complex of agricultural remains on the north side of Menstrie Glen. Sequences of enclosure are evident, for example at the centre of the photograph where the junction of the two oval fields has been remodelled. At the left edge of the photograph a field bank has been ploughed down by rigs that show a discontinuity midway along their length indicating two distinct ploughing episodes, perhaps in the first half of the 18th century.

HOUSE STYLE AND GUIDELINES FOR AUTHORS

Title

The title of the paper should be short and meaningful.
A summary or abstract if given should follow, preceding the text.

Text

Presentation and style should be concise and designed to appeal to the educated layman. It should be in typed form with ample margins, on one side of A4 size paper. Only words to be printed in italics e.g. Latin names of species or titles of publications, should be underlined. Computer prepared text to be preferably also on disk and saved as rich text format (RTF).

Citations in the text are generally to be given by author's name followed by year e.g. Jones (1978); (Marwick 1967 p62); Brown (1975) and Gray (1978). Similarly for sources or notes such as newspapers or archive citations e.g. (*Stirling Journal* 26th April 1890); (ibid 10th May 1890); (Scottish Record Office AD58/48/74). Double brackets are to be avoided.

For historical papers citing sources or notes in text may be by number as (1). Footnotes are not desirable.

Metric measurements should be used with accepted international abbreviations, such as g (grams), mm (millimetres), ha (hectares), min (minutes), etc. Approximate non-metric equivalents may be added in brackets if desirable. Abbreviations should be given in the forms: i.e., pers. comm., ibid, e.g., viz., etc. Acronyms like RSPB should have the first mention in full and avoid punctuation e.g. UNESCO, ILP, BPO, Dr, PhD, not U.N.E.S.C.O., I.L.P., Ph.D., Dr..

Whole numbers below eleven should be in word form (ten). Quotes should be in double form, single form used for emphasis.

Notes and acknowledgements should precede the references. Appendices, addenda, errata should follow the references.

Figures, Tables and Plates

All illustrations should first be provided as photocopies and the originals made available after the paper has been accepted.

Text figures should be adequately prepared for reproduction i.e. of camera ready quality with lines sufficiently black. No drawing should be so large that it must be reduced to less than one-third of its original size.

The dimensions of the printed text page (excluding running head) should be borne in mind – viz. – 172 x 110.5 mm (6^7/$_8$ x 4^3/$_8$ in), and the full page size 210 x 148 mm (8^1/$_4$ x 5^7/$_8$ in – i.e. A5).

Lettering, numerals, etc., should be carefully drawn in black ink or inserted with transfer lettering or stencils. **Captions/legends for figures should be given on separate sheets, not inserted in the figures.**

Tables should be set out on separate sheets and given separate concise captions below.

All illustrations and photographs should be of printable quality on smooth-surfaced paper, preferably not glossy, and edges trimmed square. It is important that the background be of uniform tone and free from blemishes.

All figures, tables and plates are numbered in Arabic numerals in the form: Figure 1 etc., and referred to thus in the text. They will generally be printed after the text – if not then the position of each figure, table or plate relative to the text should be indicated in the margin.

References

References should be listed alphabetically by author. Authors' names are not capitalized. The full title and year of the work should be given. Titles of papers are decapitalized but not of books. Book titles should be in italics. Titles of journals should be given in full with volume number and inclusive pagination. References to books should include the publisher and place of publication. Citations in the text are to be given as described above under **Text**.

Examples of references:

Marshall, S.M., Nichols, A.G. and Orr, A.P. 1939. On the growth and feeding of young herring in the Clyde. *Journal of the Marine Biological Association of the United Kingdom* 23, 427-455.

Russell, F.S. and Younge, C.M. 1928. *The Seas.* 397pp. F. Warne, London.

Proofs

Proofs should be corrected **in pencil** and returned **with the original manuscript** within ten days. After acceptance of the paper by the Editorial Board there should normally be no text or illustration changes. Changes in context at this time may be charged.

Enquiries and offers of papers to

Lindsay Corbett, Secretary/Editor, Forth Naturalist and Historian, University of Stirling FK9 4LA or 30 Dunmar Drive, Alloa FK10 2EH. Tel. 01259 215091.

or to

Neville Dix, Editor *The Forth Naturalist and Historian,* c/o Dept. of Biological Sciences, University of Stirling, Stirling FK9 4LA.

Full name, address and telephone details should be provided with the paper.

Addresses: Authors and Reviewers

P. J. Ashmore, Historic Scotland, Longmore House, Salisbury Place, Edinburgh, EH9 1SH.

M. Boardman and A. Seaman, Eamonn Wall & Co., 15 West Burnside, Dollar, FK14 7DP.

L. Corbett, Secretary of the Forth Naturalist and Historian, University of Stirling, FK9 4LA or 30 Dunmar Drive, Alloa, FK10 2EH.

D. Cowley, RCAHMS, John Sinclair House, 16 Bernard Terrace, Edinburgh, EH8 9NX.

Maria Devaney, Smith Art Gallery and Museum, Dumbarton Road, Stirling, FK8 2RQ.

G. A. Dixon, 3 Ronald Place, Stirling, FK8 1LF.

C. D. I. G. Forrester, 31 Station Avenue, West Ewell, Surrey, KT19 9OD.

S. J. Harrison, Environmental Science, University of Stirling, FK9 4LA.

C. J. Henty, Psychology Dept., University of Stirling, FK9 4LA.

R. L. Hills, Stanford Cottage, 47 Old Road, Mottram, Cheshire, SK14 6LW.

J. S. Kinross, 10 Quay Road, Charlestown, Cornwall, PL25 3NX.

R. McCutcheon, The Bookshop, 51 Baker Street, Stirling, FK8 1AA.

D. S. McLusky, Biological Sciences, University of Stirling, FK9 4LA.

I. Oxley, Institute of Maritime Studies, University of St Andrews, KY16 9AJ.

R. and C. Page, Kingarth, Airthrey Road, Stirling, FK9 5PH.

Angus Smith, 9 Braehead Grove, Bo'ness, EH51 0EG.

Archie Smith, 16 Katrine Crescent, Callander, FK17 8JS.

L. Stott, 10 Trossachs Road, Aberfoyle, FK8 3SW.

Erratum

The Ancient Bridge of Stirling: The Continuing Search. R. Page. *Forth Naturalist and Historian* vol. 20. The diagrams for figures 1 and 2 on p117 should be reversed.

THE FORTH NATURALIST AND HISTORIAN

The Forth Naturalist and Historian (FNH) is an informal enterprise of Stirling University. It was set up in 1975 by several University and Central Regional Council staff to provide a focus for activities and publications of environmental, heritage and historical interest for the Forth area comprising the local authority areas of Stirling, Falkirk and Clackmannshire.

The promotion of an annual environment symposium called *Man and the Landscape* has been a main feature, and 1998 is its 24th year, with the theme Woodlands – past, present,future.

The annual *Forth Naturalist and Historian* has since 1975 published numerous papers, many being authoritative and significant in their field. They include annual reports of the weather, and of birds in the locality, also some book reviews and notes. These volumes (21 as of 1998) provide a valuable successor to that basic resource *The Transactions of the Stirling Field and Archaeological Society,* 1878-1939. Five year contents/indexes are available, and selected papers are published in pamphlet form, while others eg. Ashfield Factory Village, The Weather and Bird Reports and Flora papers may be available as reprints.

A major publication is the 230 page *Central Scotland – Land, Wildlife, People* 1994. A natural history and heritage survey, and a basic resource in schools throughout the area, it is also available in the form of a CD-Rom, *Heart of Scotland's Environment* (HSE).

Other FNH and associated publications still in print include – *Mines and Minerals of the Ochils, Airthrey and Bridge of Allan; The Making of Modern Stirling; Woollen Mills of the Hillfoots; The Ochil Hills – landscape, wildlife, heritage –* an introduction with walks; *Doune – historical notes; Doune in picture postcards; Alloa Tower and the Erskines of Mar;* and the *Lure of Loch Lomond – a journey round the islands and environs.* Several of these are in association with Clackmannanshire Field Studies Society. Godfrey Maps have collaborated in producing old Ordnance Survey large scale maps of the 1890's for some 20 places in the area.

Offers of papers/notes for publication, and of presentations for symposia are ever welcome.

Honorary Secretary/Editor Lindsay Corbett,
University of Stirling, FK9 4LA, and 30 Dunmar Drive, Alloa.
Tel: 01259 215091. Fax: 01786 494994. E-mail: LindsayCorbett@stir.ac.uk
Web: http://www.stir.ac.uk/theuni/forthnat/